D0183649

Edexcel PE for GCSE

JAN 15

Edexcel PE for GCSE

endorsed by edexcel

Sue Hartigan

DYNAMIC LEARNING

HODDER EDUCATION
AN HACHETTE UK COMPANY

Orders: please contact Bookpoint Ltd, 130 Milton Park, Abingdon, Oxon OX14 4SB. Telephone: (44) 01235 827720. Fax: (44) 01235 400454. Lines are open from 9.00 – 5.00, Monday to Saturday, with a 24-hour message answering service. You can also order through our website www.hoddereducation.co.uk.

British Library Cataloguing in Publication Data
A catalogue record for this title is available from the British Library

ISBN: 978 0 340 98 328 7

First Published 2009
Impression number 10 9 8 7 6 5 4 3 2 1
Year 2014 2013 2012 2011 2010 2009

Copyright © 2009 Sue Hartigan

All rights reserved. No part of this publication may be reproduced or transmitted in any form or by any means, electronic or mechanical, including photocopy, recording, or any information storage and retrieval system, without permission in writing from the publisher or under licence from the Copyright Licensing Agency Limited. Further details of such licenses (for reprographic reproduction) may be obtained from the Copyright Licensing Agency Limited, Saffron House, 6–10 Kirby Street, London EC1N 8TS.

Hachette UK's policy is to use papers that are natural, renewable and recyclable products and made from wood grown in sustainable forests. The logging and manufacturing processes are expected to conform to the environmental regulations of the country of origin.

Cover photo © Tetra Images/Alamy
Illustrations by Barking Dog Art and Tony Jones/Art Construction
Typeset by Pantek Arts Ltd, Maidstone, Kent
Printed in Italy for Hodder Education, an Hachette UK Company, 338 Euston Road, London NW1 3BH

BLACKBURN COLLEGE
LIBRARY
Acc. No. BB58265
Class No. 613.7 HAR
Date JAN 15

CONTENTS

ACKNOWLEDGEMENTS

Sue Hartigan is extremely grateful to Jan Simister (senior examiner) for her help and generosity of ideas when compiling this text and to the unknown reviewer at Edexcel for suggested amendments.

The author and publishers would like to thank the following for permission to reproduce their photos:

1.1	© Lars Baron/Bongarts/Getty Images
2.4	© IML Image Group Ltd/Alamy
2.5	© Jeff Greenberg/Alamy
2.6	© Glyn Kirk/Action Plus
2.7 (a)	© Harry How/Getty Images
2.7 (b)	© David Hardenberg/Getty Images
2.7 (c)	© Neil Tingle/Action Plus
2.8 (a)	© Glyn Kirk/Action Plus
2.8 (b)	© Bruno Vincent/Getty Images
2.8 (c)	© Ed Kashi/Corbis
2.8 (d)	© Chris Barry/Action Plus
2.9 (a)	© Milos Bicanski/Getty Images
2.9 (b)	© Lars Baron/Bongarts/Getty Images
2.9 (c)	© Sipa Press/Rex Features
2.9 (d)	© Sipa Press/Rex Features
2.10	© vario images GmbH & Co.KG/Alamy
2.11 (a)	© Kathy deWitt/Alamy
2.11 (b)	© Kuttig – People/Alamy
2.11 (c)	© Eliot J. Schechter/Getty Images
2.11 (d)	© INDRANIL MUKHERJEE/AFP/Getty Images
2.11 (e)	© Mike Powell/Getty Images
2.11 (f)	© Action Plus
2.13 (a)	© Jack Sullivan/Alamy
2.13 (b)	© GRAHAM STUART/AFP/Getty Images
2.14 (a)	© Mike Booth/Alamy
2.14 (b)	© Matt King/Getty Images
3.1	© Martin Cushen/Action Plus
3.2	© Lawrence Manning/Corbis
3.3	© Mark Dadswell/Getty Images
3.4	© Image Bank/Getty Images
3.9	© Glyn Kirk/Action Plus
3.11	© Neil Tingle/Action Plus
3.12	© Richard Francis/Action Plus
3.13	© Harry How/Getty Images
5.1	© Glyn Kirk/Action Plus
5.2	© Glyn Kirk/Action Plus
5.4	© author
5.5	© Glyn Kirk/Action Plus
5.8	© Glyn Kirk/Action Plus
5.9	© Chris Barry/Action Plus
5.10 (a)	© Glyn Kirk/Action Plus
5.10 (b)	© Ed Bock/Corbis
5.10 (c)	© Glyn Kirk/Action Plus
5.10 (d)	© Mike Hewitt/Action Plus
5.10 (e)	© author
5.10 (f)	© Howard Boylan/Getty Images
5.11 (a)	© Glyn Kirk/Action Plus

5.11 (b)	© Owaki-Kulla/Corbis
5.11 (c)	© Mitch Diamond/Alamy
5.11 (d)	© Gari Wyn Williams/Alamy
5.11 (e)	© author
5.12 (a)	© Neil Tingle/Action Plus
5.12 (b)	© Glyn Kirk/Action Plus
5.12 (c)	© Richard Francis/Action Plus
5.12 (d)	© Isaac Menashe/Icon/Action Plus
5.12 (e)	© Sean Garnsworthy/Getty Images
6.2	*Source*: Food Standards Agency © Crown Copyright material is reproduced with the permission of the Controller of HMSO and Queen's Printer for Scotland
7.1 (a)	© Glyn Kirk/Action Plus
7.1 (b)	© Glyn Kirk/Action Plus
7.1 (c)	© Mike Hewitt/Action Plus
7.2	© Koopman/Corbis
7.3	© Kuttig – People/Alamy
7.5	© Steve Bardens/Action Plus
7.6	© Chris Barry/Action Plus
7.7 (a)	© Steve Bardens/Action Plus
7.7 (b)	© Richard Francis/Action Plus
7.7 (c)	© Iconotec/Alamy
7.7 (d)	© Image Source Black/Alamy
7.7 (e)	© GlowImages/Alamy
7.7 (f)	© PA Archive/PA Photos
7.8 (a)	© Warren Morgan/Corbis
7.8 (b)	© Neil Tingle/Action Plus
7.8 (c)	© Neil Tingle/Action Plus
7.8 (d)	© Dorling Kindersley/Getty Images
7.8 (e)	© Neal Haynes/Action Plus
7.8 (f)	© Image Source Pink/Alamy
7.9 (a)	© Richard Francis/Action Plus
7.9 (b)	© Nick Laham/Allsport/Getty Images
7.9 (c)	© Glyn Kirk/Action Plus
7.9 (d)	© Glyn Kirk/Action Plus
7.9 (e)	© Glyn Kirk/Action Plus
7.9 (f)	© Mike Hewitt/Action Plus
8.10	© Neil Tingle/Action Plus
8.11	© Glyn Kirk/Action Plus
9.2	© Glyn Kirk/Action Plus
9.7	© Martin Cushen/Action Plus
10.3 (a)	© Glyn Kirk/Action Plus
10.3 (b)	© Neil Tingle/Action Plus
10.3 (c)	© Glyn Kirk/Action Plus
10.5	© Glyn Kirk/Action Plus
11.2	© Chris McGrath/Getty Images
11.3	© Glyn Kirk/Action Plus
11.4	© Richard Francis/Action Plus
11.5	© Scott Barbour/Getty Images
11.6	© Science Photo Library
11.7	© Glyn Kirk/Action Plus
11.8	© Glyn Kirk/Action Plus
12.2	© Adek Berry/AFP/Getty Images
Table 10.3 (a)	© Glyn Kirk/Action Plus
Table 10.3 (b)	© Richard Francis/Action Plus
Table 10.3 (c)	© Action Plus
Table 10.3 (d)	© Richard Francis/Action Plus
Table 10.3 (e)	© Glyn Kirk/Action Plus

INTRODUCTION

The purpose of this book is to provide you with the essential information you need for the written examination in GCSE Physical Education. ***Edexcel PE for GCSE*** should help you in planning your Personal Exercise Programme (PEP) and increase your knowledge about factors affecting the sports performer, as well as help you to make the right choices towards achieving a healthy, active lifestyle.

Split into two sections, the book closely follows the format of the Edexcel exam specification. If you are studying the Short Course, you will currently not be tested on Section 1.2 Your healthy, active body (Chapters 7 to 11). But please check with your teacher as this could change. If you are following the Long Course for GCSE Physical Education, you will find all the content of ***Edexcel PE for GCSE*** suitable for you.

Section 1.1 covers the key concepts and key processes of Physical Education, and includes chapters on what is a healthy, active lifestyle and how physical activity can become an important part of your life.

Section 2 covers the physical aspects of how a healthy, active lifestyle impacts upon your body. Finally, Chapter 12 provides you with some revision questions to check your progress on what you have learned.

Success in examinations is a combination of your teacher's expertise, your own motivation and ability as a student, and accessibility to the appropriate resources. Written by an expert examiner, ***Edexcel PE for GCSE*** contains resources that will not only support and help you to prepare thoroughly for your exams, but challenge you at whatever level of ability you are now. In addition to learning the theory, if you want a high grade in this subject, you must be able to apply your answers directly to sport. Therefore, ***Edexcel PE for GCSE*** provides you with examples of how to apply your knowledge to help you get started.

Within ***Edexcel PE for GCSE*** you will find that every chapter offers a wide range of learning resources, with each resource signposted throughout by a distinctive icon in the text. These are:

Learning goals to keep you on track with the requirements of the Edexcel exam specification

Examiner's tips to provide you with good examples of all-important exam techniques

Actions for you to complete whatever your level of ability

Key words that provide you with clear definitions of complex physiological and technical phrases

Questions to prepare you for the types of questions that you can expect in the GCSE exam

Homework questions to check your understanding of the topics already covered in the chapter you have just read

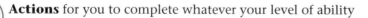

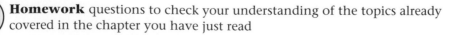

Useful websites to top up your knowledge in important areas of the Edexcel specification

Edexcel PE for GCSE is written in a clear, highly readable way that will help you to understand and learn about Physical Education. By using the materials and resources available within ***Edexcel PE for GCSE*** you will be well on your way to preparing not just for your Edexcel exam, but also for a healthy, active life.

Sue Hartigan
2009

SECTION 1

HEALTHY, ACTIVE LIFESTYLE

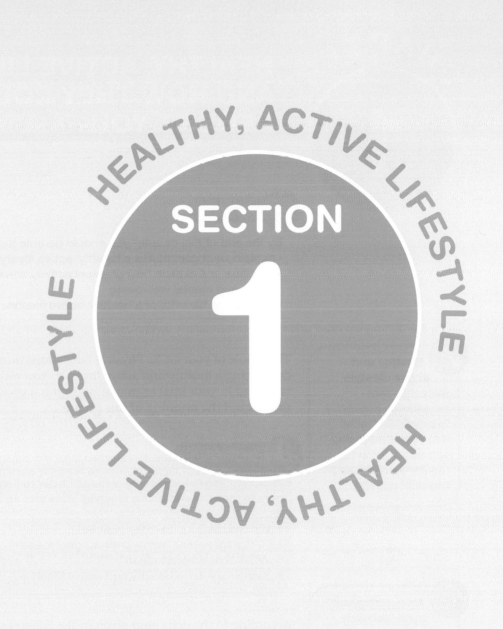

CHAPTER 1

HEALTHY, ACTIVE LIFESTYLES AND HOW THEY COULD BENEFIT YOU

GOALS

By the end of this chapter you should be able to:
- explain what constitutes a healthy, active lifestyle
- describe and explain how physical activity enhances an individual's physical, social and mental well-being
- classify the benefits of a healthy, active lifestyle as social, physical or mental.

Healthy and active lifestyle
A lifestyle that contributes positively to physical, mental and social wellbeing and which includes regular exercise and physical activity.

The whole of your GCSE Physical Education course will focus on the idea of developing a healthy and active lifestyle. You will see this phrase throughout this book and in your final examination so it is a good idea to make sure you understand the meaning of this phrase.

ACTION 1

In pairs, answer the three questions below to help you understand the key phrase 'healthy and active lifestyle'. This should help you to answer the fourth question.

1 What does it mean to be healthy?
2 How might being active improve your health?
3 What does lifestyle mean?
4 Explain the term healthy and active lifestyle.

www.sportengland.org/se_workplace_health_final_copy.pdf
Focuses on the workplace but gives clear guidance on the need for active lifestyles.

www.kidshealth.org/kid/stay_healthy/
A good site for providing tips on physical and mental health for young people.

www.healthyschools.gov.uk/Default.aspx
Provides links to meeting the ECM agenda of staying healthy.

According to the definition given in the Edexcel specification, an active, healthy lifestyle is:

> a lifestyle that contributes positively to physical, mental and social wellbeing and which includes regular exercise and physical activity.

In other words, it is a way of being healthy and feeling good about ourselves as a result of the choices we make relating to how we live our lives, for example choices about what we eat, whether we are active or not, if we are active, whether we have a good balance between activity and rest, and whether we smoke. The websites listed in the margin provide additional information on this important topic.

ACTION 2

Read the three descriptions below and discuss whether the schoolboys are leading an active and healthy lifestyle. You may find it helpful to complete Table 1.1 first before discussing.

DESCRIPTION 1

Jake plays football every Sunday with his friends but often does not play as well as he should as he regularly goes out at the weekends until 3 or 4 in the morning.

DESCRIPTION 2
Ashley completes his homework on time and seldom goes out, so always gets a minimum of eight hours' sleep a night. He chooses not to smoke but does not exercise.

DESCRIPTION 3
Imran does not play in any school teams but enjoys playing active video games with his friends. He does not smoke and is careful about his choice of food at lunchtime, opting for baked food rather than fried.

	ASPECTS OF DESCRIPTION THAT RELATE TO AN ACTIVE, HEALTHY LIFESTYLE	ASPECTS OF DESCRIPTION THAT INDICATE THE BOYS' LIFESTYLE IS **NOT** AN ACTIVE AND HEALTHY LIFESTYLE
Jake		
Ashley		
Imran		

Table 1.1 What makes an active and healthy lifestyle?

Individuals join clubs and take part in physical activity for the benefits it brings. Probably the best way to understand this is to think about your own and other people's reasons for taking part.

Figure 1.1

The benefits of physical activity are normally grouped as follows:

- mental – to do with the mind, our psychological health
- physical – to do with the body, our physical health
- social – to do with the way we interact with others, our social health.

Very often benefits can overlap from one category to another. For example, if you are overweight you might take part in physical activity to slim down a little. This has an obvious physical benefit (you lose weight), but could also have a mental benefit (you feel better about yourself because you have lost some weight).

In your exam you might be asked to list some benefits of physical activity and categorise them. It is also likely that you will be expected to explain how physical activity actually brings about this benefit. For example, we have already seen that a benefit of physical activity is feeling good or better about yourself. This is a mental benefit. The explanation for this is that when exercising aerobically researchers believe there is an increase in the levels of serotonin (a chemical) in the brain – this chemical makes us feel good. Because this feeling of well-being is associated with aerobic exercise it is sometimes referred to as 'runner's high' or 'jogger's high'. Have you experienced this 'feelgood' factor after aerobic activity?

ACTION 3

Use Table 1.2 to list the reasons you have for taking part in physical activity (try to think of at least four reasons).

REASON/BENEFIT

Table 1.2 My reasons for taking part in physical activity

ACTION 4

Compare your list with someone else's in your PE group and add any relevant different answers to your list.

ACTION 5

Compare your combined list with the list in Table 1.3. This list was also created by a group of PE students. Are there any different benefits?

REASON/BENEFIT	CATEGORY OF BENEFIT
Lose weight	Physical
Relieves my stress/helps me to relax	
I need a physical challenge	
I am good at it	
Gives me better muscle definition	
Improves my health	
Gives me something to do	
Improves my confidence/self-esteem	
I develop an aesthetic appreciation of the sport	
I like to compete	
Makes me less tense	
Meet my friends	
Improves my fitness	
Stops me getting into trouble	
Good way of meeting boys/girls	
Helps me to learn how to cooperate with others	

Table 1.3 Reasons for taking part in physical activity

When deciding on a category of benefit use the 'obvious' category; don't try to make this to complicated. If related to other people (friends; team work) classify as social; mental health (stress relief; competition; motivation) link to mental and the rest is physical!

ACTION 6

Working on your own or with a partner, look at Table 1.3 and categorise each of the benefits as with a physical, social or mental benefit of physical activity. How many of the benefits could have appeared under more than one category? Compare your answers with those given in Table 1.4

REASON/BENEFIT	CATEGORY OF BENEFIT
Lose weight	Physical
Relieves my stress/helps me relax	Mental
I need a physical challenge	Mental or Physical
I am good at it	Mental
Gives me better muscle definition	Physical
Improves my health	Physical
Gives me something to do	Mental
Improves my confidence/self-esteem	Mental
I develop an aesthetic appreciation of the sport	Mental
I like to compete	Mental
Makes me less tense	Mental
Meet my friends	Social
Improves my fitness	Physical
Stops me getting into trouble	Social benefit, but not an individual social benefit
Good way of meeting boys/girls	Social
Helps me to learn how to cooperate with others	Social

Table 1.4 Categorising the reasons for taking part in physical activity

ACTION 7

Look at Table 1.4 and try to explain how physical activity could bring about each of the stated benefits. Compare your explanations with those given in Table 1.5

Table 1.5 gives explanations of how the various benefits may be achieved.

REASON/BENEFIT	CATEGORY OF BENEFIT	EXPLANATION (HOW BENEFIT IS ACHIEVED)
Lose weight	Physical	Doing more exercise than normal, so burning off more calories to reduce weight
Relieves my stress/ helps me relax	Mental	By taking my mind off the things that are worrying me
I need a physical challenge	Mental	Mental – sense of achievement gained from doing something physical. Very important for those who do little physically during their normal day, e.g., people who work in offices. One reason why events such as the London Marathon are so popular is because people enjoy the physical challenge of training for such an event Physical – increase in fitness as a result of the additional physical work
I am good at it	Mental	Can improve people's confidence/self-esteem if they are seen as 'good' at something, especially if they are not viewed in this way at other times
Gives me better muscle definition	Physical	Through continued use muscles can develop strength and fat stores can be depleted (with an appropriate diet and training programme). Both of these factors would make the muscles easier to see (clearer muscle definition)
Improves my health	Physical	There are many possible health benefits to exercise, e.g., reduction in blood pressure and cholesterol, reduction in chances of weight-related illness
Gives me something to do	Mental	With something positive to do that you enjoy, you are unlikely to feel bored
Improves my confidence/self-esteem	Mental	You feel good for a number of reasons: you are having fun, you enjoy the challenge, you are not bored and possibly because of the endorphins released or increased serotonin levels when involved in long, continuous exercise. Once you feel good, you feel better about yourself and so your confidence/self-esteem improves
I develop an aesthetic appreciation of the sport	Mental	Most people enjoy watching a skilful performance and can appreciate the 'beauty' of that performance. This does not just refer to activities such as gymnastics or dance; it can be equally valid when watching skilful play in rugby or football, for example
I like to compete	Mental	I feel good if I win; it allows me to focus on something else and use up some of my energy
Makes me less tense	Mental	I relieve stress through doing a different activity, by taking my mind off my problems
Meet my friends	Social	My friends play the same sport as I do, so I see them at training or matches
Improves my fitness	Physical	Regular training will result in the body adapting to the new level of work we are asking it to do. These changes could include increased strength, increased cardiovascular fitness and many more, and are discussed in more detail in Chapter 5
Stops me getting into trouble	Social, but not just an individual social benefit	By stopping me getting bored and giving me something definite to do
Good way of meeting boys/girls	Social	Members of the opposite sex play sport and it is a good way of meeting people with similar interests
Helps me to learn how to cooperate with others	Social	Through working with team mates, coaches and other members of the club I learn how to cooperate with others

Table 1.5 Explanations for how the benefits of exercise may be achieved

If you are asked to explain how a benefit of physical activity is achieved make sure you give sufficient detail in your answer. For example, if asked to explain how fitness is increased, an answer stating 'by exercising regularly' would be insufficient to gain a mark because without increasing the intensity, fitness will only be maintained – not increased. A good answer would be 'taking part in regular training where there is a gradual increase in the intensity of training so the body adapts to the greater demands placed on it.'

HOMEWORK

Interview people from other age groups and the opposite gender to you (these should be family members, friends, friends' families and peers at school other than your PE class) to see why they take part in physical activity. Categorise their answers as mental, physical or social and explain how these benefits are achieved. Present your findings to the rest of the group.

CHAPTER 2

INFLUENCES ON YOUR HEALTHY, ACTIVE LIFESTYLE

GOALS

By the end of this chapter you should be able to:
- **identify key influences on achieving sustained involvement in physical activity**
- **explain the opportunities available for involvement in physical activity in a range of roles and the qualities required for these roles**
- **explain the sports participation pyramid**
- **describe initiatives developed to provide opportunity for involvement in physical activity.**

Influences on your healthy, active lifestyle
An influence is anything that can impact on what you do; it affects your behaviour or thoughts/feelings about something

KEY INFLUENCES ON ACHIEVING SUSTAINED INVOLVEMENT IN PHYSICAL ACTIVITY

So what makes us want to get involved in physical activity? OK, we know from Chapter 1 that it is 'good' for us physically, mentally and socially, but so are a lot of other things that we don't necessarily want to do: revision, early nights, not eating junk food, not smoking. Yet many people still do these things, so what actually influences whether we take up physical activity or not? In the previous chapter you had to list why you participated in physical activity; this chapter asks a slightly different question. Rather than why you participate in terms of the benefits physical activity brings, you need to understand why you started playing the activities you did in the first place. For example, if you play football, why do you play this rather than rugby (or vice versa)?

ACTION 1

Make a list of all the physical activities you are involved in. List all of the activities on the board for the group, keeping a tally of how many times a specific activity is mentioned.

Look at the list you have compiled for Action 1.

- Is each activity played by the same number of people?
- If not, what activities are more popular?
- Why are these activities played more?
- Why are some activities participated in less?

It might help if you think about why you started playing the activities you did.

ACTION 2

Go back to the list on the board of all the activities that your group participates in. Extend the list to include the activities your family and friends play.

ACTION 3

Look at Figures 2.1, 2.2 and 2.3. What seems to be influencing the amount of practical activity in these figures?

If you have added any extra activities to your list:

- What is different about the added activities?
- Are there any reasons why they were not on the list that you and the rest of the group participate in?

What activities are missing?

- Make a list of any other activities you can think of that are not listed already.
- Why don't you do any of these activities?

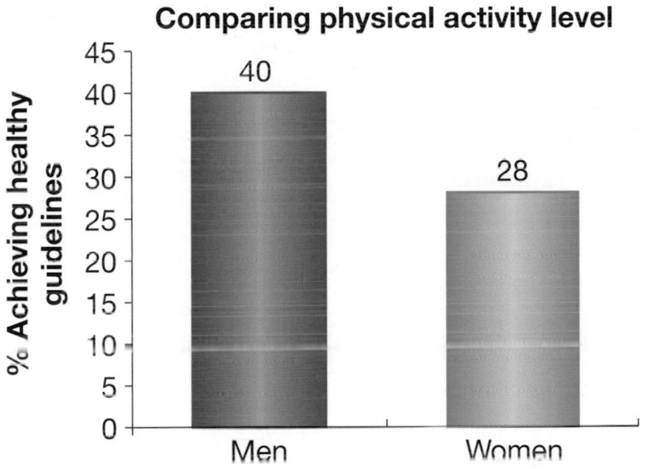

Figure 2.1 Comparing physical activity level between men and women

Source: Health Survey for England, 1998

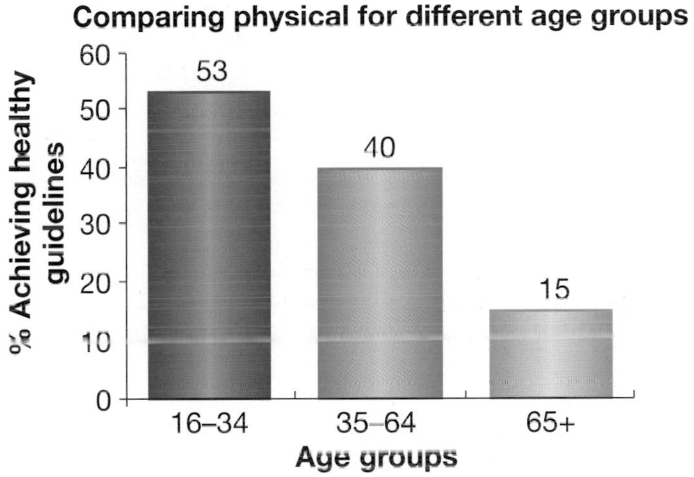

Figure 2.2 Comparing physical activity level between age groups

Source: Health Survey for England, 2007

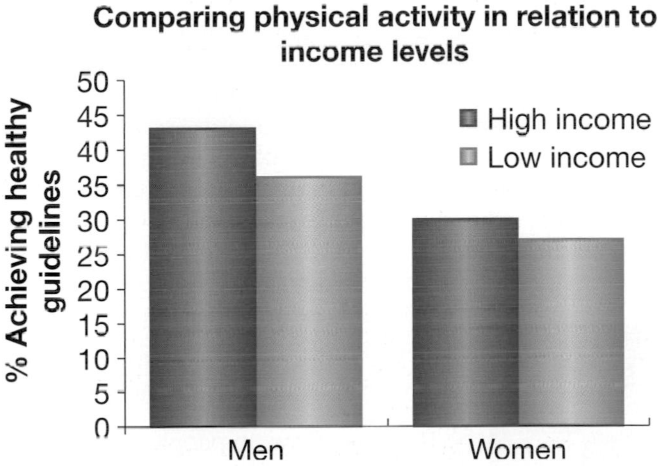

Figure 2.3 Comparing physical activity level in relation to income

Source: Health Survey for England, 2007

Hopefully you are starting to build a list of the factors that can influence your choice of physical activity. Check your ideas against those given in Tables 2.1 and 2.2.

	PERCENTAGES
Health isn't good enough	47.0
Not really interested	18.4
It's difficult to find the time	18.2
I am too old	2.7
It costs too much	2.1
I wouldn't enjoy it	1.8
Never occurred to me	1.6
No one to do it with	1.1
I am too lazy	1.1
Other reasons	5.9

Table 2.1 Main reasons for non-participation in physical activity

Source: Taking Part Survey, 'Taking Part: The National Survey of Culture, Leisure and Sport', The Department for Culture, Media and Sport

	PERCENTAGES
Less busy	39.3
Cheaper admission prices	11.0
People to go with	8.7
If I had more free time	6.4
Better playing facilities	3.5
Improved transport/access/ more cycle lanes	3.2
Help with childcare/crèche facilities	3.1
If there were more/better variety of local facilities	3.0
Better facilities, e.g., cafés, changing rooms	2.8
Longer opening hours	2.7
If the weather was better	2.5
If I had better health	1.7
Better equipment	1.6
Support for my specific needs, e.g., injury or disability	1.3
Safer neighbourhood	1.2
Better information on what to do	1.0
If I had more motivation/more energy	1.0
Other reasons	5.8

Table 2.2 Factors which would increase participation

Source: Taking Part Survey, 'Taking Part: The National Survey of Culture, Leisure and Sport', The Department for Culture, Media and Sport

Some of the reasons given in Table 2.1 for not participating seem to be related to lack of motivation/fun/enjoyment. For example, 'Not really interested', 'Never really occurred to me', 'I wouldn't enjoy it', 'I am too lazy'. If this were your attitude how might it change if your friends all took part in the activity? Would you be more motivated because you knew they were going? Would you have fun because your friends were there? Would it motivate you to be more energetic even if you felt lazy? If so then people can influence your choice of whether to be active or not and also the activity you participate in.

Figure 2.4 Family influence on choice of physical activity

The key influences impacting on participation you need to be aware of for your examination are as follows.

1 **People**. How do people influence your choice of activity?
   (a) Family – this can have an impact. If your parents play sport you are likely to play sport as they will introduce you to physical activity as you grow up and you are likely, at least initially, to play the same sports that they do.
   (b) Peers – your friends can have an impact. In your original list, how many activities do you participate in that match what your friends do? If your friends are all going to play badminton at lunchtime it is likely that you will go with them; similarly, if your friends do not participate in sport there is less reason for you to do so.

Figure 2.5 Peer influence on choice of physical activity

Figure 2.6 Influence of role model on choice of physical activity

(c) Role models – these are people you respect. They can be teachers(!), older family members, sports 'stars'. If someone you respect takes part in a specific activity this will encourage you to get involved in the same activity.

2 **Image**. How does the image of an activity influence your choice?

(a) Fashion – this relates to clothing: what clothes do you have to wear for an activity? Would it make any difference? Based on the clothing, which of the sports or positions in Figure 2.7 would you play?

Figure 2.7 Sports clothing, does it impact on choice of activity?

(b) Media coverage – the second aspect of image is whether the activity is 'fashionable' in the media: is it a really popular activity at the time? Activities such as football have remained popular, but other activities such as squash, volleyball, table tennis and tennis vary in popularity over time. Tennis tends to be more popular when it is televised for Wimbledon. Have a look in your local park: how many more people seem to play tennis when Wimbledon is on the television? Why might the media influence what we play?

E QUESTION

Which of the activities in Figure 2.8 would you be interested in?
What has helped you make that choice? Do you know others who play the sport and have told you it is good? Is it in the media? Does it have a positive image? Does it look exciting/interesting?

Culture
The set of shared attitudes, values, goals, and practices that characterises a group.

3 **Culture.** Choice of activities will vary depending on the following:

(a) Age – why might the activity you choose vary with age? Look at Table 2.3. Which age group do you associate with each activity? Explain your choice.

Figure 2.8 Influence of the media on activity choice

ACTIVITY	ASSOCIATED AGE GROUP YOUNG/OLD/ANY	REASON FOR CHOICE
Football		
Cricket		
Badminton		
Crown green bowls		
Rambling		
Horse riding		
Skiing		
Snow-boarding		

Table 2.3 Physical activity and age

(b) Disability – clearly if you have a disability it may limit how you participate in an activity, although given the right resources (see below) most sports can be adapted.

(c) Gender – although more activities are becoming recognisable as a sport for both sexes, there is still gender bias associated with some sports. Look at the activities in Table 2.4. Which sex do you associate with each activity? Why?

ACTIVITY	SEX ASSOCIATED WITH ACTIVITY MALE/FEMALE/EITHER	REASON FOR CHOICE
Football		
Cricket		
Badminton		
Boxing		
Aerobics		
Horse riding		
Ballet		
Gymnastics		

Table 2.4 Physical activity and gender

Figure 2.9 Physical activity and disability

(d) Race – in the way that women and men are still associated with some sports, the same applies to race. There are no physical reasons why one group of people should be inherently better at one activity than another, but due to stereotyping some people believe that different races are better at different sports. Because of this people from different races are often encouraged (through the media and significant others) into particular sports. Look at Table 2.5. What race do you associate with each activity? Remember you are dealing with stereotypes – it is up to you and your class to try to break some of these stereotypes! Look at the image in Figure 2.10. The competitor in the picture is 95 and competing in an international championship, representing Australia!

ACTIVITY	RACE ASSOCIATED WITH ACTIVITY ASIAN OR ASIAN BRITISH/BLACK OR BLACK BRITISH/WHITE/ANY	REASONS FOR CHOICE
Athletics – sprinting		
Cricket		
Badminton		
Boxing		
Athletics – long distance		
Horse riding		
Men's hockey		
Tennis		

Table 2.5 Physical activity and race

Stereotypes
These are commonly held, oversimplified, pre-conceived ideas about a person or group. They can be positive or negative.

Figure 2.10 Stereotypes in sport

4 **Resources.** Choice of activities will vary depending on the following:
(a) Access – facilities might exist, but there might be age restrictions preventing access, or they might be too expensive, thus denying you access (for example, a golf club would be a lot more expensive than a council-owned facility, so although the facility existed you still could not access it). Similarly, if the facility is a bus ride away, or not accessible by public transport, you still cannot get to the facility.
(b) Availability – you might be restricted due to the facility's opening hours or the times that classes for beginners are available. For example, if you wanted to take up a new sport and beginners' taster sessions were on Saturdays but you had a part-time job on a Saturday, you could not go and so would be unlikely to take up the activity. Availability also relates to finding appropriate venues – if you cannot find a club to play at, you won't be able to play. For example, you might like to try skiing, but if you don't live near a mountain or an artificial ski slope it will be very difficult to get involved in this physical activity.
(c) Location – as mentioned above, the facilities might exist but might be too far away to get to easily, thereby reducing your chances of participating in that activity.
(d) Time – a lot of people say they would participate in something if only they had the time to do so.

5 **Health and well-being**. Choice of activities will vary depending on the following:
(a) Illness – clearly if you are unwell you cannot participate on a temporary basis.
(b) Health problems – some health problems will prevent participation in some types of activities and so limit the person's choice. This does NOT mean, however, that all physical activity needs to stop. People with health problems would consult their GP to establish an appropriate level of physical activity.

6 **Socio-economic**. Choice of activities will vary depending on the following:
(a) Cost – some activities are more expensive than others due to playing fees (hire of court, for example), cost of equipment or travel to venue. Those people with a limited amount of disposable income (not much cash!) will not have as big a choice of activities as those with more money.
(b) Status – some activities are associated with different socio-economic groups within society. Look at Table 2.6. Who do you associate with the activities?

ACTIVITY	STATUS (SOCIO-ECONOMIC GROUP) ASSOCIATED WITH ACTIVITY HIGHER/LOWER/EITHER	REASONS FOR CHOICE
Cricket		
Football		
Rugby		
Boxing		
Rowing		
Athletics		
Polo		
Tennis		

Table 2.6 Physical activity and status

ACTION 4

Look at the images in Figure 2.11. Rank order the activities, placing at number 1 the activity you would most like to take part in. Look at your rank order. Which of the key influences listed above (1–6) have had an impact on your selection?

Figure 2.11 What's your favourite activity?

OPPORTUNITIES FOR INVOLVEMENT IN PHYSICAL ACTIVITY AND THE QUALITIES REQUIRED

ACTION 5

List the different ways you can be involved in physical activity and feedback to the rest of the group.

The obvious way of being involved in physical activity is through performance, i.e., taking part in the activity itself, but there are a number of other roles in physical activity. Each of these roles requires certain characteristics and qualities. Do you have what it takes to become:

1 A performer? (Fitness, motivation, determination, ability, opportunity, knowledge of the activity)
2 A coach/leader? (Motivational, able to analyse performance, good communicator, ability, enthusiasm)
3 Official – referee/umpire? (Clear, fair, fit, calm, knowledgeable about the rules, confident, good communicator, patient)

Although in elite sport individuals are paid high wages for taking on any of these roles, at grass roots level most activities can continue because of the number of people who take on these roles on a voluntary basis, for example all the people who freely coach junior football teams, officials at junior athletics competitions and so on.

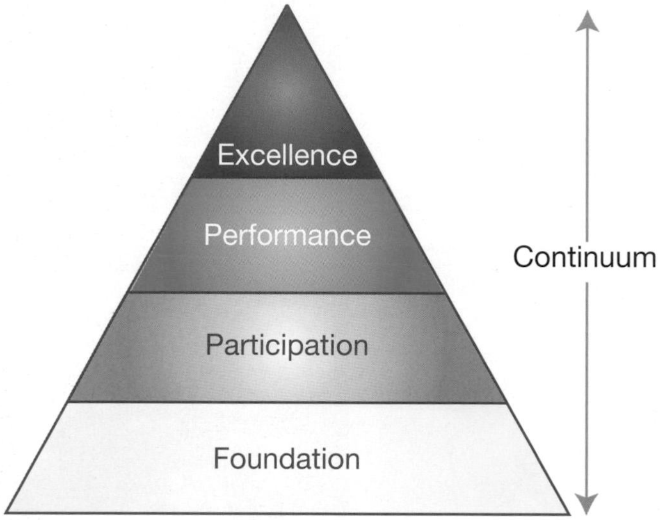

Figure 2.12 The sports participation pyramid

THE SPORTS PARTICIPATION PYRAMID

The government wants more people to be active to boost their health and one way of increasing activity is through increasing participation in sport. The sport participation pyramid is a model of sport development. The purpose is to have the necessary structures and processes in place at each level so that people are encouraged and enabled to take part in sport and work their way 'up' the pyramid until they find their own level.

This model was devised in 1988; since then other models have been produced, but the concept is the same. This model has four stages, starting from the base.

Foundation

This is where people are introduced to the activity, for example being introduced to games through a 'taster' multi-sports session for the first time in a physical education lesson in primary school. During this stage people learn the basic skills and develop an understanding of the activity. This stage is the broadest because more people go through this stage than any of the other stages. Some people will remain at this stage while others progress from this to the next stage.

Participation

People progressing to this stage of the pyramid do so because they choose to use their leisure time to take part; this is non-compulsory. It could be during break times at school or out of school hours in the evening or at the weekend, possibly with family, friends or external clubs. People will play competitively at this stage but at a lower level than at the performance stage.

Performance

The performance level is where skills are developed through coaching and competition. Players would be in the higher division competitive leagues, playing at regional level.

Excellence

The excellence stage is the top of the pyramid. There are relatively few performers here compared with the numbers at the base of the pyramid at the foundation level. People at this stage have reached national and international level.

Some people therefore make the transition from one level in the pyramid to another:

Figure 2.13 From participation to excellence

Figure 2.14 Moving up the sports participation pyramid

Figure 2.14a+b

INITIATIVES DEVELOPED TO PROVIDE OPPORTUNITY FOR INVOLVEMENT IN PHYSICAL ACTIVITY

Initiative
This is an idea or a plan that is put forward to address an issue

We have already decided at the start of this chapter that it is not enough just to tell people that activity is good for them, they have to be encouraged and the opportunities need to be available if the number of people leading an active lifestyle is to increase. Therefore the government and some of its supporting organisations have devised and launched many different initiatives to try to increase opportunities for becoming or remaining involved in physical activity. For example:

1 **Policies relating to minimum involvement in PE and sport**
In 2004 the government set the target that by 2010 all schoolchildren would have two hours of PE a week. More than £1.5 billion was invested in physical education and school sport over the next five years (up to 2008) to help achieve

this target and in 2008 80 per cent of schools had already achieved this target. So a long-term ambition is also in place. This is the hope that by 2010 all children will be offered at least four hours of sport every week: two hours of PE and sport at school and an additional two or more delivered by school, community and club providers.

2 **PE School Sport and Club Links (PESSCL)**

This is one of the initiatives in place to try to help achieve the target set for minimum involvement in physical activity (number 1 above). By developing links between schools and clubs the hope is that children will be introduced to a sport at school, enjoy it and then be able to continue to play and improve at a local club. By making the links known and making it easy/natural to play at a club it is hoped that more children will find it easy to play for clubs rather than playing at school and then stopping. Clubs might set up specific development days to encourage children from schools to come along, set up more junior teams to allow more competition or send coaches into schools to raise the profile of the sport.

Figure 2.15 The SSCo logo

3 **School Sport Partnerships**

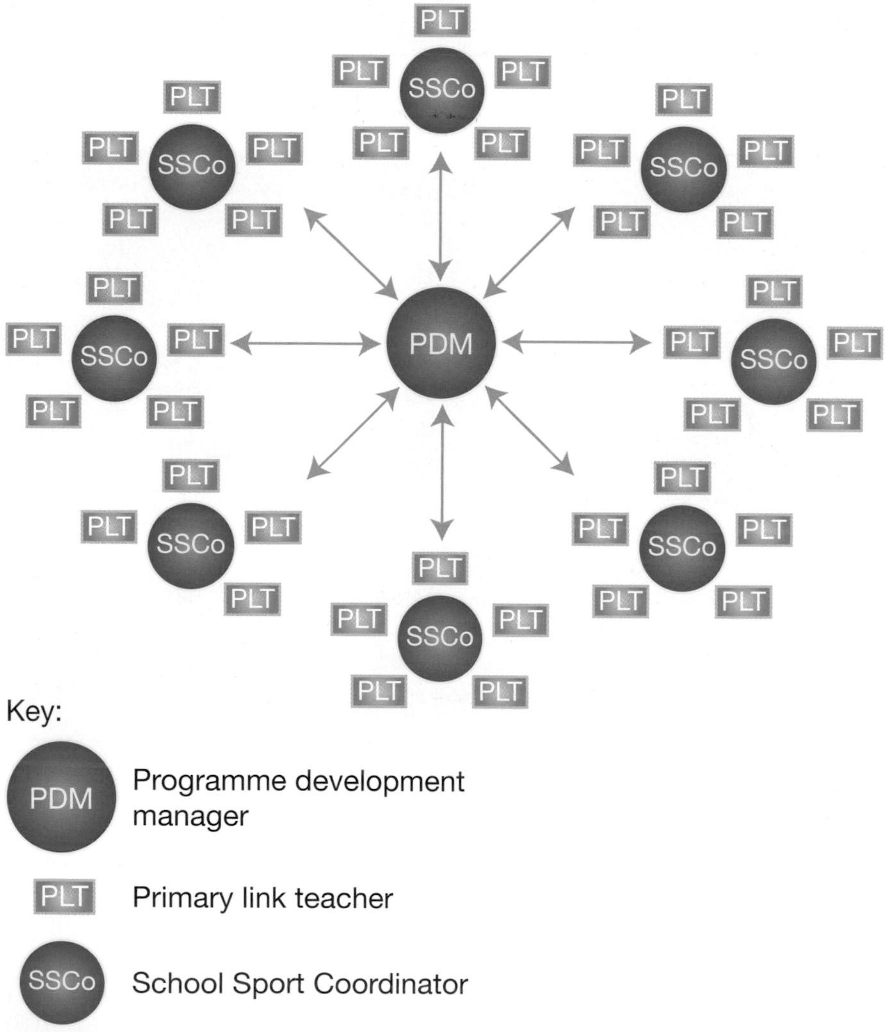

Figure 2.16 A typical School Sport Partnership cluster

Source: www.teachernet.gov.uk/-img/partnership%20Model.gif

E QUESTION

Who is the SSCo at your school?

ACTION 6

Draw the SSP cluster for your area.

These are one of the ways of delivering the PESSCL strategy. In September 2006 there were 450 School Sport Partnerships. They are groups of schools clustered around a sports specialist college (see Figure 2.16). The partnership receives additional funding to allow staff time to develop more sporting opportunities for students. Staff in these schools are given time to work with local primary schools to develop after-school activities and links with the local community and sports clubs.

4 **Sport England's Start, Stay, Succeed initiative**

This initiative was in response to Sport England's objective to make England an active and successful sporting nation. It was part of the national plan for sport in 2004. In order to achieve success we need to:

- **Start** – increase participation in sport in order to improve the health of the nation, with a focus on priority groups
- **Stay** – retain people in sport and active recreation through an effective network of clubs, sports facilities, coaches, volunteers and competitive opportunities
- **Succeed** – achieve sporting success at every level.

5 **Youth Sports Trust TOP programmes**

TOP programmes are designed to give young people (up to the age of 18) of all abilities and in particular target groups (those with disabilities, teenage girls and gifted and talented athletes) the chance to make the most of the opportunities that PE and sport can bring.

6 TOP Play and TOP Sport works by providing additional training for teachers (of children aged 4–9) to improve the quality of teaching PE and school sport. Sainsbury's TOP Activity (Active Kids) aims at 7–11 year olds through out-of-school activities. The activities covered are not traditional games as there is already scope for these; the idea here is to provide a wider choice to interest more children. Activities range from cheerleading to frisbee. TOP Link is aimed at 14–16 year olds (you!) to encourage you to organise and manage sport or dance festivals in local primary schools. TOP Sportsability tries to integrate young disabled and non-disabled students through a variety of sporting challenges.

You should be familiar with these examples for your examination, but don't forget that initiatives change over time, so it is worth checking on websites to get the most up-to-date information. Some websites you might want to use are provided here.

www.sportengland.org.uk
Look out for the initiative Grow Sustain Excel: 2008–2011

www.skillsactive.com/
Provides information on the active leisure and learning sector.

www.uksport.gov.uk/
Provides information about UK Sport's mission 'to lead sport in the UK to world class success' and how this is managed.

www.youthsporttrust.org/
Useful site giving details of initiatives that enhance quality of PE and sporting activities.

www.sportsaid.org.uk/
Provides detail of how Sports Aid works with NGB to provide crucial funding for young sportsmen and women.

www.sportingchampions.org.uk/
Gives detail of Sport England initiative which brings world-class athletes in contact with young people to inspire them to participate in sport.

www.sportscoachuk.org/
Provides up-to-date information on the development of the UK coaching system.

www.dh.gov.uk/en/index.htm
Have you seen the 2009 Change4Life campaign?

www.teachernet.gov.uk/teachingandlearning/subjects/pe/nationalstrategy/
Provides detail of the national PE, School Sport and Club Links strategy.

CHAPTER 3

EXERCISE AND FITNESS AS PART OF YOUR HEALTHY, ACTIVE LIFESTYLE

GOALS

By the end of this chapter you should be able to:

- explain the terms health, fitness and exercise
- explain how health, fitness and exercise relate to a balanced, healthy lifestyle and performance in physical activity
- state and explain the components of health-related exercise and their relative importance to different physical activities (cardiovascular fitness, muscular strength, muscular endurance, flexibility, body composition)
- state and explain the components of skill-related exercise and their relative importance to different physical activities (agility, balance, coordination, power, reaction time and speed).

There is often confusion over the difference between health and fitness. For this part of the course you need to understand these terms, define them and explain the difference between them. You also need to know the components of health-related exercise and skill-related fitness and their importance to sporting activities.

ACTION 1

Think about the two words **health** and **fitness.** Copy and complete Table 3.1 by listing the words that you associate with someone who is healthy or fit. Use these words to give a definition of health and another for fitness, and feedback your answers to the rest of the group.

FITNESS	HEALTH

Table 3.1 Understanding health and fitness

Health
A state of complete physical, mental and social well-being and not merely the absence of disease or infirmity.

HEALTH

In 1948 the World Health Assembly defined health as:

a state of complete physical, mental and social well-being and not merely the absence of disease or infirmity.

(*Source*: http://en.wikipedia.org/wiki/Health January 2009)

Although there are many varied definitions of health, all reflect this basic concept, i.e., health relates to more than just the physical. Think back to the first chapter about the benefits of physical activity – the importance of exercise should be clear to you as it can have physical, social and mental benefits, all of which should have a positive effect on our health, especially if coupled with sensible lifestyle choices as well. Not surprisingly, this early general definition of health is the one that you need to learn for your examination.

ACTION 2

Look at Figures 3.1 and 3.2. Who is the healthiest? Justify your answer.

People who do not take part in sport can still be healthy provided they have some form of regular physical activity and interests to help them stay healthy, socially and mentally. Through adopting a healthy lifestyle (balanced diet, regular sleep, non-smoking, limited alcohol consumption, physical activity), they can still maintain their health.

Figure 3.1 Elite performer in action

Figure 3.2 Non-athlete – sedentary

Fitness
The ability to meet the demands of the environment.

FITNESS

Fitness is defined by the Edexcel examination specification as:

the ability to meet the demands of the environment.

This means that you are able to cope with the amount of physical work you need to do. (All subsequent definitions are taken from the Edexcel specification unless otherwise indicated.)

Figure 3.3 Elite performers 'at work' on the track

Figure 3.4 Non-athletes 'at work' in the office

ACTION 3

Look at Figures 3.3 and 3.4. Who is the fittest? Justify your answer.

If someone is never expected to do any more physical work than walk to the bus stop and they can do this without undue stress, then they are as 'fit' as the sports performer who trains regularly to meet the demands of their 'work'. The difference in fitness would become obvious only if the non-athlete were suddenly expected to do the same amount of physical work as the athlete.

Your answer to the last part of the question on this page may be 'yes', but it may not be. It is possible to be fit while not being healthy. Can you think of an occasion when this might be the case? Many fit athletes may temporarily be unhealthy if they are suffering from a cold or similar infection, or an illness such as diabetes, or even in extreme cases the initial stages of major diseases such as cancer. An increase in fitness does improve the chances of being healthy (see chapters in Section 2), but it cannot guarantee good health.

Exercise
A form of physical activity done to maintain or improve health and/or physical fitness; it is not competitive sport.

E QUESTION

Who is the fittest person in your class? How do you know they are the fittest? When does it become obvious that they are the fittest? Is the fittest person in your class also the healthiest?

EXERCISE

Exercise is:

a form of physical activity done to maintain or improve health and/or physical fitness; it is not competitive sport.

As you can see, this definition links health with fitness, recognising the benefits of physical activity mentioned in Chapter 1 – through exercise we can develop our physical, mental and social health and our physical fitness. A detailed

www.bbc.co.uk/schools/gcsebitesize/pe/exercise/0_exercise_health_rev1.shtml
Links the work of this chapter with Chapter 1, 4 and 5, and has additional activities for you to complete.

explanation of the effects of exercise and training on the body can be found in the second section of this book.

PERFORMANCE

Performance
How well a task is completed.

Although you will not be asked to define performance you need to understand the term so that you can see how health, fitness and exercise can impact on it. Performance is:

how well a task is completed.

Performance can be anything from excellent to poor; it is simply a way of describing the quality demonstrated in a practical activity. We judge performances in gymnastics and diving, and how well a task is completed has a direct effect on the score for that performance. Although other performances are not judged in the same way (e.g., an individual's performance in a football match), how well they complete their tasks is still likely to have an impact on the final score, especially if we consider the team's performance, i.e., how well the team completed its tasks (such as attacking and defending).

ACTION 4
Can you see any link between the terms health, fitness, exercise and performance? Discuss your ideas with a partner and feedback to the group.

HEALTH-RELATED EXERCISE

In order to improve our health and fitness, we can exercise and improve the components of health-related exercise. Increasing our fitness should have a positive impact on our performance, provided we improve the right components of health-related exercise for our activity.

There are five components of health-related exercise, as shown in Figure 3.5.

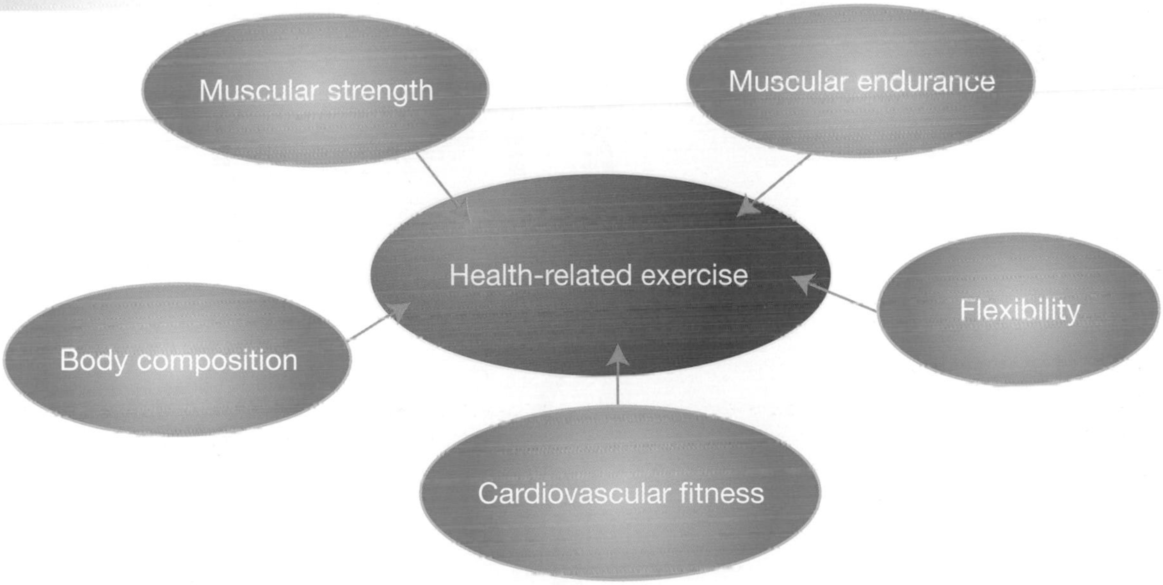

Figure 3.5 The components of health-related exercise

If a question asks you to define a term, make sure you use the definitions stated in this book or the exam board specification.

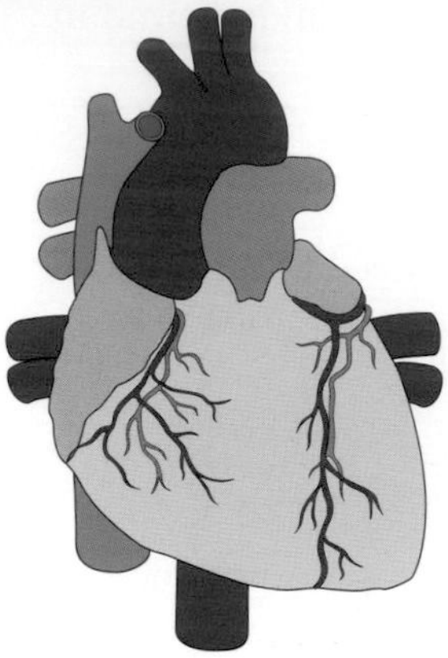

Figure 3.6 The heart

Cardiovascular fitness

Cardiovascular fitness is a very important aspect of health-related exercise. The definition you need to learn is:

the ability to exercise the entire body for long periods of time.

The cardiovascular system achieves this by supplying the body with enough oxygen so that it can continue to release energy, provided the intensity of the activity is not too great. For example, marathon runners are able to exercise their bodies for long periods of time (in excess of two hours), but you would not expect a sprinter to be able to sprint for the same amount of time. This is because their bodies do not have enough time to release energy using oxygen, as they are working anaerobically. This is explained further in Chapter 5.

Cardiovascular fitness is very important to a healthy lifestyle. The word cardiovascular can be split into two – see Figure 3.7.

Figure 3.7 Cardiovascular fitness

Cardiovascular fitness is concerned with the heart, the blood and the blood vessels. It is important to health, as there are a number of cardiovascular diseases that could result in death if left unchecked. High blood pressure, heart attacks and strokes are all caused by disorders in the cardiovascular system. Fortunately, a health-related programme of exercise can help maintain cardiovascular fitness.

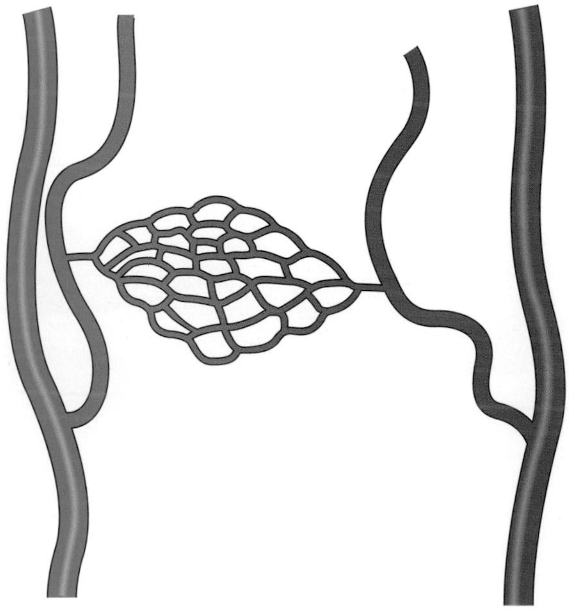

Figure 3.8 The blood and blood vessels

Muscular strength

This is a very important component for many activities and is:

the amount of force a muscle can exert against a resistance.

For example, in cricket, the greater the muscular force (generated by using the strength of their muscles) the batsman uses to hit the ball, the further the ball should go. In gymnastics, gymnasts use muscular strength to support their own body weight in a variety of techniques and balances, e.g., a handstand or a balance on the rings.

Figure 3.9 Elite gymnast holding position on the rings

Muscular endurance

This means:

the ability to use voluntary muscles many times without getting tired.

Athletes with high levels of muscular endurance can repeatedly use their muscles to continue working throughout their events, allowing them to maintain the quality of their performance.

E QUESTION

Why would a badminton player need high levels of muscular endurance in his or her arms?

ACTION 5

Make a table and list as many sports as you can think of in the first column. Tick each of the sports that you think requires a high level of muscular endurance. Write a short statement to explain why you have selected each sport.

Body composition

This is defined as:

the percentage of body weight which is fat, muscle and bone.

This refers to the chemical make-up of the body, in particular the amount of the body that is made up of fat compared with the amount of the body that is made up of lean body mass (e.g., bone and muscle). For example, if you weighed 63.5kg and had 15 per cent body fat, it would mean that your body had 9.5kg of fat and 54kg of lean body mass.

It is important to all of us to have some body fat in order to allow the body to function properly. The percentage of fat that we have compared with lean body mass will have an impact on our performance in sport. Table 3.2 shows some percentage body fat scores for performers in different activities.

FEMALE % BODY FAT	MALE % BODY FAT	SPORT
12–18%	12–15%	Baseball
20–27%	6–12%	Basketball
12–18%	8–15%	Field and ice hockey
12–18%	6–14%	Rowing
14–24%	9–12%	Swimming
12–20%	8–10%	Track – runners
10–18%	7–12%	Track – jumpers
20–28%	14–20%	Track – throwers
10–15%	5–12%	Triathlon
16–15%	11–14%	Volleyball

Table 3.2 Percentage fat scores in different activities
Source: www.brianmac.demon.co.uk/fatcent.htm (January 2009)

E QUESTION

Performers in which sport have the greatest body fat score? Which group has the lowest? Can you draw any conclusions about the relationship between the type of activity and percentage body fat? Why might it be an advantage in some activities to have a lower percentage of lean body mass (which weighs more than body fat)?

FLEXIBILITY

Flexibility is important to all athletes to differing degrees. Flexibility is:

the range of movement possible at a joint.

An increase in flexibility can help prevent muscle injury in some activities where the intensity of work can be explosive, e.g., in sprinting and football, and is very important in performers in their teens as the body is still growing and developing. Increased flexibility in tennis players will allow for further stretching to reach the ball, but too much flexibility could lead to greater risk of joint injury as the joint becomes less stable. Regular stretching will increase the flexibility of a joint,

ACTION 6

Identify how each of the components of health-related exercise is used by the performer in Figure 3.9

although the actual shape of the joint (the way the bones fit together) will limit the amount of movement possible.

HOMEWORK

Learn the components of health-related exercise. It might help if you try to think of a mnemonic or a story to link the components. For example, the statement 'Buy Many Football Club Managers (to improve health)' does not make much sense until you realise that it is one way to remember the initials of each of the components of health-related exercise.

- B Body composition
- M Muscular endurance
- F Flexibility
- C Cardiovascular fitness
- M Muscular strength

This also reminds you that the statement is to do with health-related exercise and not the components of skill-related fitness covered next.

As with health-related exercise, the components of skill-related fitness have an important impact on performance. All components are normally useful to all performers, but some are more significant than others depending on the sporting activity. The components of skill-related fitness cannot be improved through training as easily as the components of health-related exercise; in fact, improvement in these areas is often due to anticipation and experience rather than improvement in the basic skill.

As with the previous section on health-related exercise, it might be helpful to think of a statement to help you remember the components of skill-related fitness (e.g., Mike skilfully RAPS on his CB). It is better if you can think of your own statement as this will make it more meaningful and therefore easier to remember for your exam.

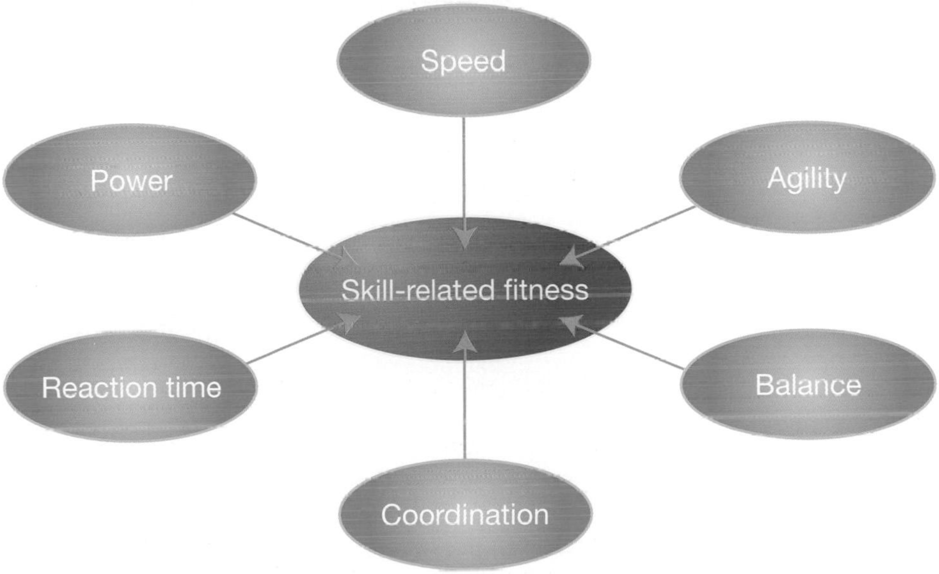

Figure 3.10 Components of skill-related fitness

SPEED

Speed is:

the differential rate at which an individual is able to perform a movement or cover a distance in a period of time.

Fortunately you do not have to learn this definition, provided you understand what it means. We all know that speed is to do with how fast we move and we easily accept that speed is important to sprinters so that they can cover the distance of their race quicker than anyone else and win. But speed is equally important to a javelin thrower. Speed in this case refers to how quickly the thrower can move the arm during the throwing action: the faster the arm speed, the further the javelin should go.

E QUESTION

What other sports performers require speed? Give examples of how these performers use speed.

REACTION TIME

Reaction time is:

the time between the presentation of a stimulus and the onset of a movement.

This is a very important component in activities where decisions have to be made quickly, e.g., when you realise your badminton opponent has just played a disguised shot and you need to move forward to the front of the court to retrieve it, or when the ball hits the top of the net in tennis and bounces off at an unusual angle. The stimulus is the thing you need to respond to, in this example the tennis ball; the onset of movement is when you start to move.

E QUESTION

What is the stimulus for the badminton player?

E QUESTION

Other than at the start of a race, reaction time is not so important for swimmers or track and field athletes. Can you explain why?

ACTION 7

Give an example of the use of reaction time in an activity other than badminton or tennis.

BALANCE

Balance is described as:

the ability to retain the body's centre of mass (gravity) above the base of support with reference to static (stationary), or dynamic (changing), conditions of movement, shape and orientation.

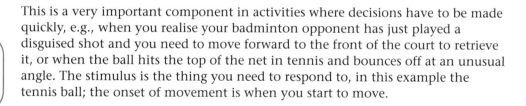

Once again it is not necessary to learn this definition provided you understand it. Gymnasts obviously use balance to hold themselves still when performing techniques such as handstands and headstands. This is static balance, but other performers need dynamic balance. For example, for a rugby player swerving through the opposition en route to a try, or resisting a tackle and continuing on their run, and a hockey player changing direction at full speed, dynamic balance is critical.

Figure 3.11 Player maintains balance despite opposition trying to unbalance them

AGILITY

Agility is:

the ability to change the position of the body quickly and to control the movement of the whole body.

Agility is about changing your direction quickly. Hundred-metre sprinters do not need agility in their event as they run on a straight track. Games players do need agility, as they are constantly changing direction to avoid being tackled by their opposition, or to put themselves in a position to tackle, or to move into space. Once again, the demands of the activity dictate which components of skill-related fitness are important to the performer.

Figure 3.12 Discus thrower during spin coordinates timing and the movement of feet and arms to get more distance on the throw

COORDINATION

This refers to the ability to use two or more body parts together.

This skill-related component is obviously very important in physical activity. Activities that require the performer to strike an object, e.g., volleyball, require good hand–eye coordination. The body needs to be able to move the hand so that it arrives in the correct place to strike the ball and it cannot do this without good co-ordination. Other activities, such as football, require good foot–eye coordination so that the foot arrives in the correct place to make contact with the ball.

Other examples of coordination include the combined use of arms and legs in sprinting to make sure the sprinter reaches the maximum speed, or the discus thrower coordinating his move across the circle and the movement of his arm to get the best possible speed, height and angle of release so that the discus travels further.

POWER

Power is defined as:

the ability to do strength performances quickly.

Power is also expressed as an equation: power = strength × speed. To be powerful, then, you need both speed and strength. A gymnast uses power during the tumbling routine, where their movements explode from the floor. A tennis player will use power during the service when the racket arm is brought through quickly and with strength, so that the racket hits the ball with power to make the serve difficult to return.

Figure 3.13 Zac Purchase and Mark Hunter scull strokes.
Source: Xinhua

ACTION 8

The performers in Figure 3.13 use the components of skill-related fitness in their performance. List the components they use and rank them in order in terms of their importance to the activity (with 1 being the most important and 6 being the least important). Justify your rank order.

ACTION 9

Complete Table 3.3 by selecting the important components of skill-related fitness for each of the activities listed. Give an example of how the component is used in the activity.

HOCKEY	GYMNASTICS	STEEPLECHASE
Reaction time		
Agility		
Power		
Speed		
Coordination		
Balance		

Table 3.3 Applying components of skill-related fitness to activities

http://www.brianmac.co.uk/conditon.htm
Contains lots of relevant information to support your course, BUT if terms differ, use the ones in this book as they relate directly to you course).

HOMEWORK

Think about the activities for which you are being assessed in your practical work. What are the important components of skill-related fitness for these activities? How do they help your performance?

ACTION 10

Make a list of the components of health-related exercise and skill-related fitness you need to improve your performance in one of your activities. Justify your choices.

ACTION 11

Complete the crossword. All of the answers can be found in this chapter.

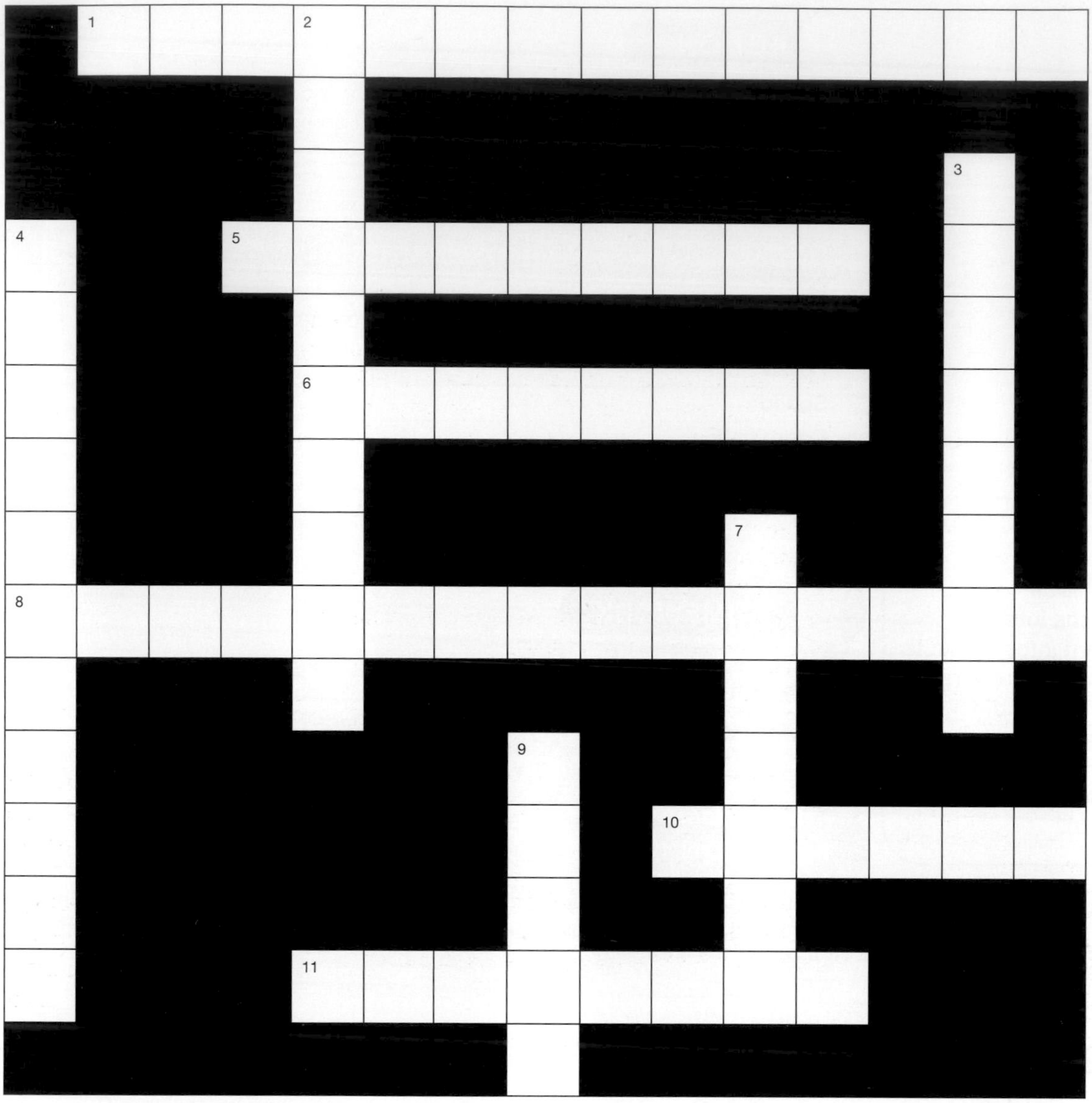

Health, Fitness, Exercise and Performance

Across:

1 This type of activity is used to develop strength (6, 8)

5 Exercising without oxygen (9)

6 Performers in this event need to make sure they develop their strength to help them increase the distance they can throw (4,4)

8 What is the term that means the relative composition of body fat to muscle? (4, 11)

10 Sometimes confused with 7 Down, but refers to our mental, physical and social well-being (6)

11 This is carried out to improve either 10 Across or 7 Down (8)

Down:

2 Flexibility is very important to performers in this activity to help them achieve the shapes they need (10)

3 To be good in this event the athlete needs very high levels of cardiovascular fitness (8)

4 A definition of this term is 'the range of movement possible at a joint' (11)

7 Sometimes confused with 10 Across, but means that you can meet the demands of the environment (7)

9 What is the missing component of the cardiovascular system? . . . ., blood, blood vessels (5)

CHAPTER 4 PHYSICAL ACTIVITY AS PART OF YOUR HEALTHY, ACTIVE LIFESTYLE (PART 1)

GOALS

By the end of this chapter you should be able to:

- give examples of personal readiness questions (PAR-Q)
- assess personal readiness for activity (PAR-Q)
- describe fitness tests for health-related exercise and skill-related fitness
- assess personal fitness levels based on results of fitness tests
- describe, explain and apply the principles of training:
  - progressive overload
  - specificity
  - individual differences/needs
  - rest and recovery
- explain the components of the FITT principle
- explain the term reversibility
- explain the value of goal setting
- describe, explain and apply the principles of setting SMART targets.

Young Person's 'Physical Activity Readiness' Questionnaire

Dear Parent/Guardian,

There are many health benefits to be gained from regular exercise, but it is important to consider the level of health before commencing a physical exercise programme. This questionnaire aims to identify any potential health issues your child may have so that we avoid any risk of injury and can also provide appropriate exercise advice.

Young Person's Registration Information

First Name: .... Surname: ....

Address: ....

....

.... Postcode: ....

Home No: .... Mobile No: ....

Gender: Male / Female (please circle) Date of Birth: ....

The following questions relate to the health of the young person. Please read the questions carefully and provide a correct answer by circling Yes or No. Where necessary, please provide details.

			Details
Has a doctor ever diagnosed your child with a heart condition?	Yes	No	
Has your child recently had chest pains during or after exercise?	Yes	No	
Does your child ever feel faint or have spells of severe dizziness?	Yes	No	
Is your child currently receiving treatment or medication for high blood pressure?	Yes	No	
Is your child currently receiving treatment or medication for any other condition?	Yes	No	
Has your child broken any bones in the past six months?	Yes	No	
Does your child suffer from any bone or joint problems which exercise may aggravate?	Yes	No	
Does your child suffer from epilepsy or chronic asthma?	Yes	No	
Is your child diabetic? If yes, is the diabetes Type 1 or Type 2?	Yes	No	
Has your child undergone any recent surgery?	Yes	No	
Is there any other reason which has not been mentioned that may affect your child if they took part in physical activities?	Yes	No	

Continued Overleaf

Activity as part of a healthy, active lifestyle should be planned in order to be safe and effective. This chapter explains the principles that should be applied before engaging on a planned programme of exercise.

Before undertaking increased levels of exercise individuals should assess their readiness for physical activity. This is normally done through a personal readiness questionnaire (PAR-Q). The first page of an example PAR-Q is shown here.

PAR-Q
A physical activity readiness questionnaire, this is a series of questions that should be asked before engaging in increased levels of physical activity to ensure there are not health issues that should be taking into account when planning intensity of exercise.

ACTION 1

1 Research and collect copies of existing PAR-Qs from:
- Internet
- local sports centre
- your school.

2 In small groups compare the PAR-Qs.
- Are there any common questions?
- What are the questions checking?
- How would this help to judge an individual's readiness for activity?

3 Individually create your own PAR-Q based on your research.

4 Work with a partner (taking the role of coach, they take the role of participant):
- Discuss the questions on your PAR-Q, helping your partner to complete the PAR-Q.
- Discuss the results – is your partner ready for physical activity?

E QUESTION

Apart from establishing initial fitness levels, why else would you use fitness tests?

Having established through a PAR-Q that it is appropriate to increase activity levels the next step in a planned programme is to find out current fitness levels so you can plan appropriate workloads. This can be achieved through fitness testing.

Each of the components of health-related exercise and skill-related fitness identified in Chapter 3 can be 'measured' using specifically designed fitness tests.

ACTION 2

Without turning back to the previous chapter, add to Table 4.1 the missing components of health-related exercise (hint: Buy Many Football Club Managers (to improve health)) and skill-related fitness (hint: Mike skilfully RAPS on his CB).

COMPONENT OF HEALTH-RELATED EXERCISE	FITNESS TEST FOR COMPONENT
COMPONENT OF SKILL-RELATED FITNESS	**FITNESS TEST FOR COMPONENT**

Table 4.1 Fitness tests for health-related exercise

CARDIOVASCULAR FITNESS – COOPER'S 12-MINUTE RUN

- Use a 400m track (to make measuring easy) and run around it as many times as possible in 12 minutes. Measure the total distance you cover. (Although the test says this is a run, if you cannot run for 12 minutes you can complete using a mixture of running and walking.)
- Calculate the total distance covered.
- Use 'average' tables to get your rating.

AGE	EXCELLENT	ABOVE AVERAGE	AVERAGE	BELOW AVERAGE	POOR
Male 13–14	>2700m	2400–2700m	2200–2399m	2100–2199m	<2100m
Females 13–14	>2000m	1900–2000m	1600–1899m	1500–1599m	<1500m
Males 15–16	>2800m	2500–2800m	2300–2499m	2200–2299m	<2200m
Females 15–16	>2100m	2000–2100m	1700–1999m	1600–1699m	<1600m
Males 17–19	>3000m	2700–3000m	2500–2699m	2300–2499m	<2300m
Females 17–20	>2300m	2100–2300m	1800–2099m	1700–1799m	<1700m

Table 4.2 Normative data for the Cooper Test

Source: www.brianmac.co.uk/gentest.htm January 2009

CARDIOVASCULAR FITNESS – HARVARD STEP TEST

- Use a standard gym bench (45cm).
- Record resting heart rate.
- Step up and down off the bench in time to the metronome/tape for five minutes (once every two seconds).
- One minute after exercise take heart rate for 30 seconds. Record as rate 1.
- Take heart rate again after two minutes, for 30 seconds, and record as rate 2 and finally after 3 minutes for 30 seconds and record as rate 3.
- Calculate your score using the following formula:

Score = 100 * (300 seconds/ 2*(pulse1 + pulse2 + pulse3)

E.g., if rate 1 was 75, rate 2 60 and rate 3 55, your score would be as follows:

= 100*(300/2*(75 + 60 + 55)
= 100*(300/2*(190)
= 100*(300/380)
= 100*0.79
= 79

STEP TEST SCORE	RATING
> 90	Excellent
80–89	Good
65–79	High average
55–64	Low average
< 55	Poor

Table 4.3 Rating chart

Source: http://lenziepesg.googlepages.com/8.Harvard_Step_Test.doc January 2009

MUSCULAR STRENGTH – HAND GRIP STRENGTH TEST

- Using a hand grip dynamometer adjust the grip if required.
- With your elbow at your side and your lower arm at right angles to the body squeeze the dynamometer with maximum effort and hold for three seconds before releasing.
- Read dial for strength measurement. Repeat twice and take an average reading.
- Use 'average' tables to get your rating.

RATING*	MALES (KG)	FEMALES (KG)
Excellent	> 64	> 38
Very good	56–64	34–38
Above average	52–56	30–34
Average	48–52	26–30
Below average	44–48	22–26
Poor	40–44	20–22
Very poor	< 40	< 20

Table 4.4 Table for the hand grip strength test

Source: www.topendsports.com/testing/strength-about.htm January 2009

Muscular endurance can be tested through any test that requires the performer to use the same muscle or group of muscles repeatedly, for example the sit-up test. You do not need to be familiar with this test for your exam.

FLEXIBILITY – SIT AND REACH TEST

SIT AND REACH (BOYS)	AGE						
RATING	11	12	13	14	15	16	17
Excellent	34	35	36	39	41	42	45
Good	29	29	30	33	34	36	40
Average	25	26	26	28	30	30	34
Below average	21	21	20	23	24	25	28
Poor	12	13	12	15	13	11	15
	Centimetres						
SIT AND REACH (GIRLS)	AGE						
RATING	11	12	13	14	15	16	17
Excellent	37	40	43	44	46	46	44
Good	32	34	36	38	41	39	40
Average	29	30	31	33	36	34	35
Below average	24	25	24	28	31	30	31
Poor	16	15	17	18	19	14	22
	Centimetres						
Performed with feet against 12″ × 12″ × 21″ box – 23 cm at level of feet.							

Table 4.5 Sit and Reach Test

Source: http://www.exrx.net/Testing/YouthNorms.html January 2009

- Using a sit and reach box sit on the floor with your legs out straight and feet flat against the box.
- Keeping your legs straight, bend forward and push the ruler on the top of the box away from you as far as possible.
- Record your score and use 'average' tables to get your rating.

Body composition can be tested using skin fold calipers or electronic equipment that measures the percentage of the body that is fat compared with other tissue. You do not need to be familiar with these tests for your exam.

FITNESS TESTS FOR SKILL-RELATED FITNESS

Agility – Illinois Agility Run Test

- Set up test as shown in Figure 4.1.
- Start by lying on your front, hands behind the start line.
- On 'go' run the course as quickly as possible.
- Compare your score to the 'average' rating table in Table 4.6.

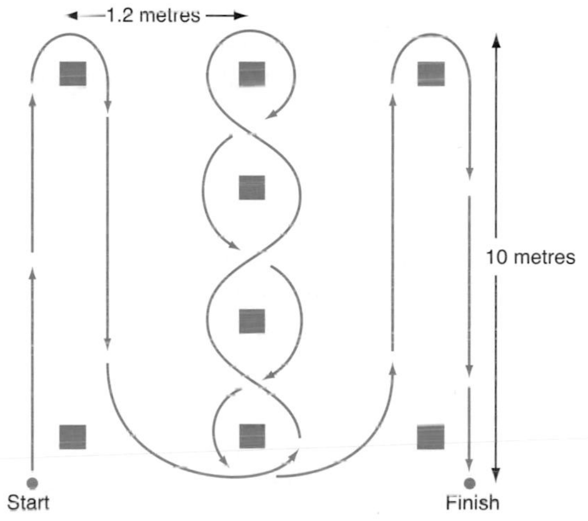

Figure 4.1 Illinois agility run text

AGILITY RUN RATINGS TIMES IN SECONDS RATING	MALES	FEMALES
Excellent	<15.2	<17.0
Good	16.1–15.2	17.9–17.0
Average	18.1–16.2	21.7–18.0
Fair	18.3–18.2	23.0–21.8
Poor	>18.3	>23.0

Table 4.6 Average rating table for the Illinois Agility Run Test

Source: www.pcworld.org/fitnesstesting/agility_run.htm, January 2009

Balance – Standing Stork Test

- Remove shoes and place hands on hips.
- Put one foot on the side of the knee of the balancing leg.
- Go on to the ball of the foot so your heel is off the floor.

- Time how long you can maintain this position without moving.
- Take the best of three attempts and compare your score to the 'average' rating chart.

HOW DID YOU DO?	SCORE (IN SECONDS)
Excellent	> 50
Good	40–50
Average	25–39
Fair	10–24
Poor	< 10

Table 4.7 Rating chart for the Standing Stork Test
Source: http://gottasport.com/weight-training/37/test-your-balance.html Janunary 2009

Coordination – Alternate Hand Wall Toss Test

- Stand 2m away from the gym/sports hall wall.
- Throw a tennis ball with your right hand against the wall and catch it with your left hand.
- Throw the ball with your left hand against the wall and catch it with the right hand.
- Repeat for 30 seconds counting successful catches.
- Compare results with the 'average' rating table in Table 4.8.

AGE	HIGH SCORE	ABOVE AVERAGE	AVERAGE	BELOW AVERAGE	LOW SCORE
15–16 years	> 35	30–35	25–29	20–24	< 20

Table 4.8 Rating table for the Alternate Hand Wall Toss Test
Source: http://www.brianmac.co.uk/coord.htm January 2009

http://www.jugglingdb.com/compendium/startjuggling/learntojuggle.html
A fun website if you want to learn to juggle.

Other tests of coordination are equally valid. For example, a 3-ball juggle test could be used. Each participant is timed juggling three balls until a mistake is made. Their time is noted and compared to other class members to establish a rating.

Power – Sergeant Jump Test (vertical jump)

- Place chalk on fingers and mark standing height on jump board (arm extended above head).
- Crouch down and leap up, marking board at top of jump (arms above head).
- Read off distance between two marks and compare with 'average' rating chart.

VERTICAL JUMP (CM ABOVE STANDING HEIGHT)		
RATING	MALE	FEMALE
Excellent	> 60	> 55
Good	50–60	45–55
Average	40–49	35–44
Fair	30–39	25–34
Poor	< 30	< 25

Table 4.9 Rating chart for the Sergeant Jump Test
Source: www.answers.com/topic/sargent-jump-test January 2009

Power – Standing Board Jump

- Stand behind line.
- Jump forward using a two-footed take-off.
- Measure the distance achieved.
- Take a further two attempts to give an average score and compare to 'average' rating table.

RATING	MALES (CM)	FEMALES (CM)
Excellent	> 250	> 200
Very good	241–250	191–200
Above average	231–240	181–190
Average	221–230	171–180
Below average	211–220	161–170
Poor	191–210	141–160
Very poor	< 191	< 141

Table 4.10 Rating chart for the Standing Board Jump

Source: http://www.topendsports.com/testing/tests/longjump.htm January 2009

Reaction time – Ruler Drop Test

- A partner holds a metre rule from one end so the rule hangs vertically between the index finger and thumb of the person being tested.
- The thumb should be level with the zero centimetre mark on the ruler.
- Catch the ruler as soon as your partner drops it.
- Measure the distance been the zero centimetre mark and the top of the thumb where the ruler was caught.
- Compare the distance (indicates time taken) to the average rating chart.

The following are national norms for 16–19 year olds.

EXCELLENT	ABOVE AVERAGE	AVERAGE	BELOW AVERAGE	POOR
< 7.5cm	75–15.9cm	15.9–20.4cm	20.4–28cm	> 28cm

Table 4.11 Normative data for the Ruler Drop Test

Source: http://www.brainmac.co.uk/rulerdrop.htm

Speed – 30m sprint

- Start from a stationary position behind the starting line.
- When signal to go is given run as fast as possible for 30m.

TIME (SECS) MALE	TIME (SECS) FEMALE	RATING
< 4.0	< 4.5	Excellent
4.2–4.0	4.6–4.5	Good
4.4–4.3	4.8–4.7	Average
4.6–4.5	5.0–4.9	Fair
> 4.6	> 5.0	Poor

Table 4.12 Average chart for the 30m sprint

Source: *Sport and PE: A Complete Guide to AS Level Study*, Hodder Arnold.

- Starter times the run.
- Compare time taken to the 'average' chart.

ACTION 3

Working with a partner:

- perform an appropriate set of warm-up exercises.
- complete a series of fitness tests and record your results for each test.
- use national rating tables and identify your strengths/weaknesses in terms of your fitness results.

ACTION 4

Complete Table 4.13 by naming the fitness test each image represents and the component of health-related exercise or skill-related fitness it is measuring.

IMAGE	NAME OF TEST	COMPONENT MEASURED
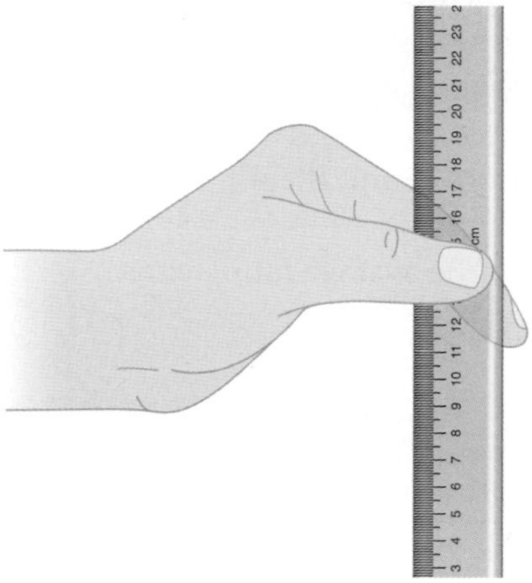		
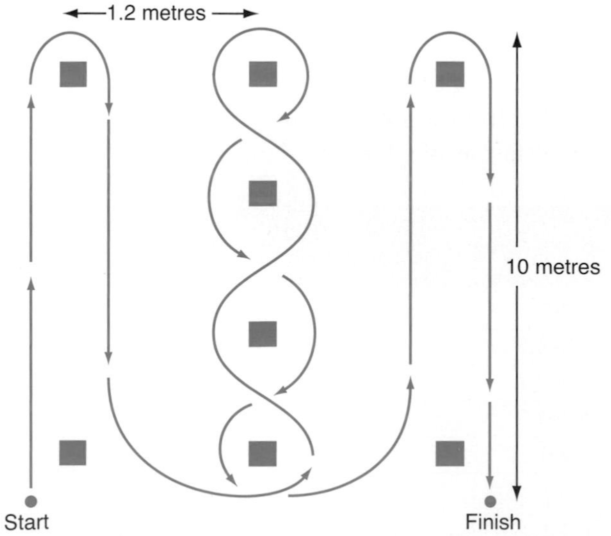		

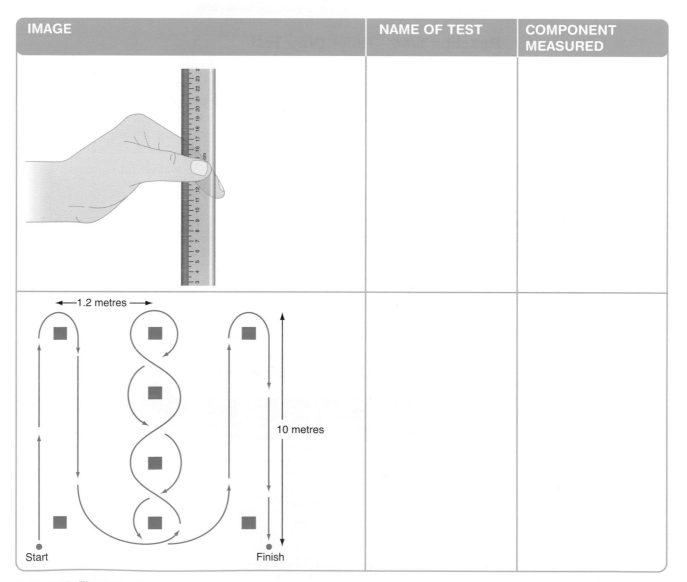

Table 4.13 Fitness testing

IMAGE	NAME OF TEST	COMPONENT MEASURED
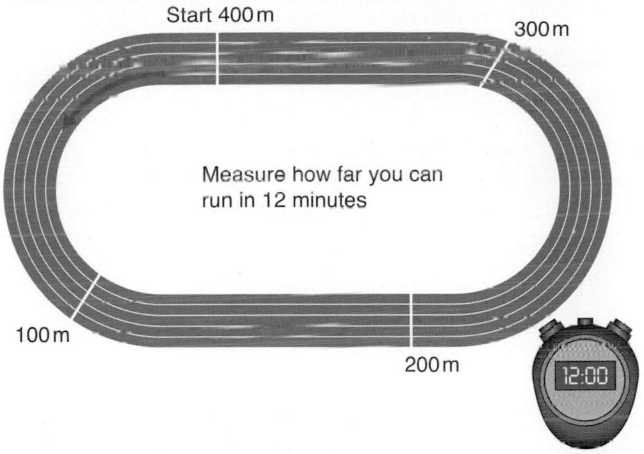		
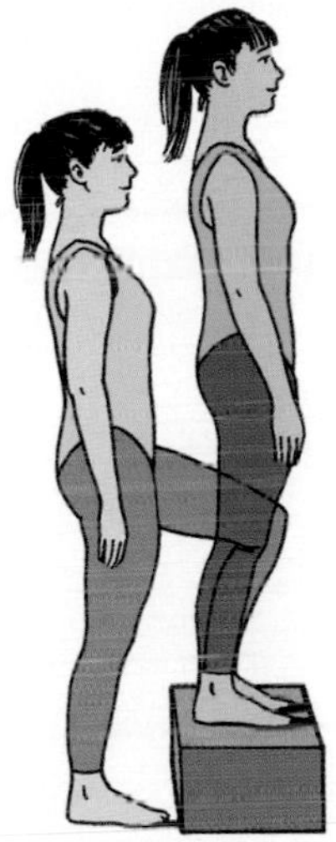		

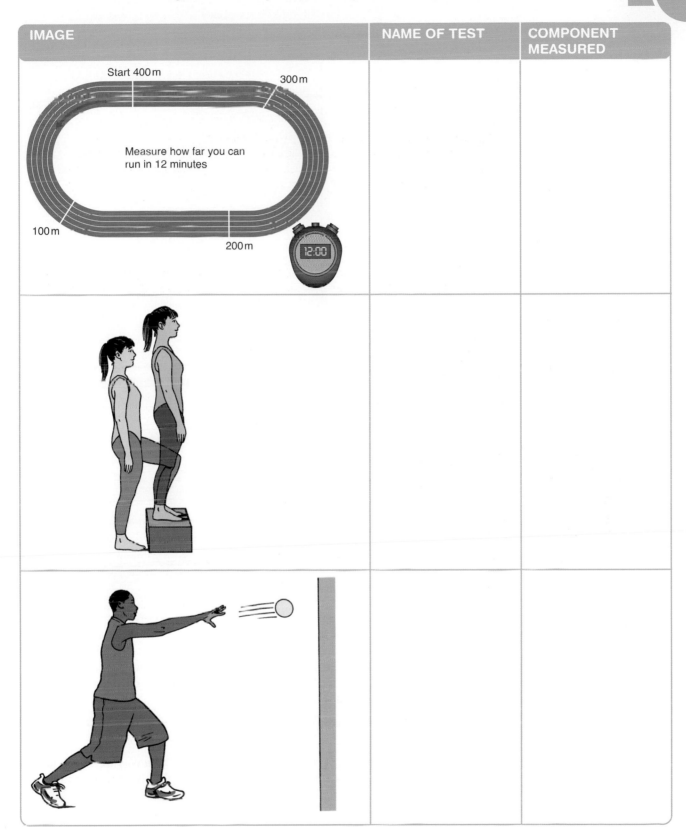

Table 4.13 *Continued* Fitness testing

IMAGE	NAME OF TEST	COMPONENT MEASURED
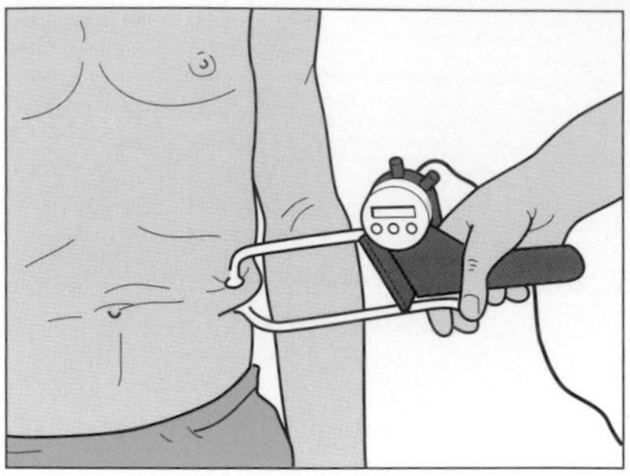		

Table 4.13 *Continued* Fitness testing

E QUESTION

Which principles of training are represented by RIPS?

R ➪

I ➪

P ➪

S ➪

Fill in the missing principles of training.

R ➪

F ➪

PRINCIPLES OF TRAINING

You need to know about the principles of training because correct application of them within your PEP should lead to an improvement in aspects of your health-related exercise. In other words, they are 'rules' which, if followed, allow your training to be more effective; this should have a positive impact on your performance in whichever sporting activity you participate and on your health, helping you lead an active and healthy lifestyle.

Figure 4.2 shows the principles of training that you are required to know for the Edexcel specification.

As with the previous chapter it might be helpful to think of a way to help you remember the components. RIPS could be used to remember the main principles that you need to apply, but unfortunately it does not cover all of the principles that you need to know.

So, we now have RIPS RF (see definitions below). This is just to help you remember the names of the principles – if you can mix the letters and come up with something that is easier for you to remember then do it!

Remembering the names of the principles is a good start, but you will also be expected to define some, explain what all of them mean, recognise them from

The principles of training listed here are those required by Edexcel; other examination boards and books might refer to other principles of training, but you need to make sure you only refer to the principles stated here as they relate to *your* specification.

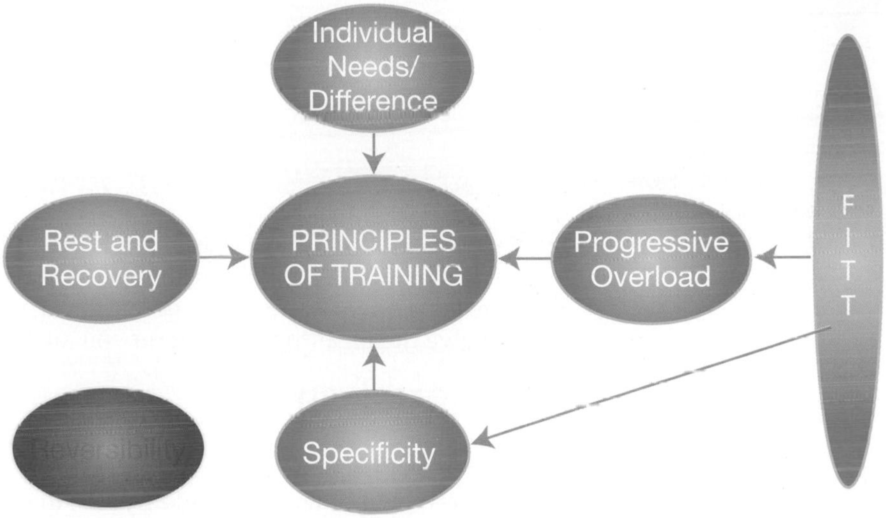

Figure 4.2 Principles of training

their description or definition and show how you might apply them in a personal exercise programme (PEP) to improve aspects of health-related exercise.

Principles of training
A set of ideas/values that should be followed in order to make training effective.

DEFINITIONS OF THE REQUIRED PRINCIPLES OF TRAINING

Rest and recovery:

Rest – *the period of time allocated to recovery.*

Recovery – *the time required for the repair of damage to the body caused by training or competition.*

Individual differences/needs:

Matching training to the requirements of an individual.

Progressive overload:

To gradually increase the amount of overload so that fitness gains occur, but without potential for injury.

Specificity:

Matching training to the requirements of an activity.

Reversibility:

Any adaptation that takes place as a consequence of training will be reversed when you stop training.

ACTION 5

Look at the four definitions above. What do you think each one means? How might each one apply to you?

FITT:

Frequency, Intensity, Time, Type (used to increase the amount of work the body does, in order to achieve overload).

EXPLANATIONS OF THE PRINCIPLES OF TRAINING

Remember that a definition is asking for something very specific, normally an exact repeat of a statement from the specification. Explanations are different. They are your interpretation of a definition. They should be in your own words but still give the meaning of the term you are being asked to explain.

Rest and recovery

It is vital that you plan adequate rest in any training programme to allow your body to recover from the physical work you are making it do and it gives a good balance between home, school and fitness, in other words it is an essential part of a healthy lifestyle. Without appropriate rest the body does not have time to:

- replenish energy stores
- repair damage to muscle tissue
- allow adaptations to muscles to take place
- relax and de-stress
- reduce feelings of physical fatigue.

But how do you know if you are doing too much? A simple checklist like the one below could be used. If you total less than 20 points you're probably not ready for an intensive workout!

Rate each statement on a 1–5 scale as follows: 1 = strongly disagree; 2 = disagree; 3 = neutral; 4 = agree; 5 = strongly agree.

1 I slept really well last night.
2 I am looking forward to today's workout.
3 I am optimistic about my future performance(s).
4 I feel vigorous and energetic.
5 My appetite is great.
6 I have very little muscle soreness.

Source: http://www.pponline.co.uk/encyc/0685.htm January 2009

ACTION 6

Research the term periodisation. How does this 'fit' with the principle of rest and recovery?

Lack of rest and recovery can lead to overtraining. This is not helpful as it can lead to you feeling depressed and lethargic, can increase the chance of injury and generally can lead to a drop in performance – not the desired effect! Recovery can be short term or long term. Short-term recovery could be a cool-down at the end of a session or working at a lower intensity in the next couple of training sessions, so that over the training week there is a balance and opportunity for recovery. Long-term recovery is the rest/recovery periods built into a seasonal training programme to make sure the performer has adequate rest so they can perform at their best at the right time for their sporting year.

ACTION 7

Explain how age, sex, sporting experience, weight, height and current level of fitness could make a difference to the training programme followed.

Individual differences/needs

This principle is referred to as individual needs in some textbooks, individual differences in others; you can use either in your examination, so remember whichever suits you best. This principle of training is similar to the principle of specificity. The difference is that this principle considers the needs of the individual rather than the needs of the sporting activity. In other words, according to the principle of specificity, two footballers could do the same training programme. (Consider Ronaldinho and Steven Gerrard, or any other two performers. Would you give them the same training programme?) By adding the principle of individual needs we should formulate a much better PEP, as the training will also consider the performer. Factors such as age, sex, sporting experience, weight, height, current level of fitness should all make a difference to the type of training programme followed. If you consider these things when forming your own PEP, then you are applying the principle of individual needs.

Progressive overload

What training do you currently do? If you wanted to apply the principle of progressive overload, what would you have to do to the amount of training you currently do? Give a specific example.

E QUESTION

Why do we need both parts of the principle of progressive overload and not just overload?

There are three critical parts to this training principle:

1 Gradually increase
2 the amount of work you normally do
3 without the potential for injury.

ACTION 8

Which of the examples in Table 4.14 demonstrate the principle of progressive overload?

In your exam you might be asked to give an example of progressive overload; if you remember these three parts to the principle it should be easy to answer this sort of question. For example, if you currently train twice a week, you would be overloading by training three times a week (this is a gradual increase, from two to three and therefore should not result in injury). The reason for overloading the body is that by making it work harder it has to adapt to the new work rate, therefore making you 'fitter' (look back at the definition of fitness in Chapter 3). These adaptations are dealt with later in the book in Chapters 7–10, but the way in which the body adapts makes it easier for the sports performer to perform well. For example, a sprinter should run faster once their body has adapted to extra physical work, because they are becoming more muscular.

EXAMPLE	PROGRESSION	ACCURATE APPLICATION OF PROGRESSIVE OVERLOAD – YES/NO?
Train twice a week	Train five times a week	
Work for 30 minutes	Work for 31 minutes	
Complete 25 repetitions	Complete 30 repetitions	
Lift 5kg	Lift 4kg	
Work at 70% of my maximum heart rate	Work at 75% of my maximum heart rate	

Table 4.14 Applications of progressive overload

Specificity

This principle is stating that you cannot just do any type of training, but that you must match your training to the needs of your sport.

E QUESTION

Would you expect the pairs of athletes in Table 4.15 to follow the same training programme? If not, why not?

PAIRS OF ATHLETES	SAME PEP – YES/NO?
Sprinter	Marathon runner
Netball player	Swimmer
Dancer	Squash player
Tennis player	Rugby player
Footballer	Footballer

Table 4.15 Training needs

ACTION 9

Consider the pairs of performers in Table 4.16. Under the 'rule' of the principle of individual needs and/or specificity, decide whether any of these performers could use the same training programme. Justify your answer.

Football goal-keeper aged 28, plays for premiership club	Midfield player aged 24, plays for premiership club	**Yes/No Justification**
International rugby player; mesomorph; below 5 ft 6 in in height; plays in fly position	International rugby player ectomorph; 6ft tall; plays in front-half position	**Yes/No Justification**
Olympic female volleyball player aged 21	Olympic male volleyball player aged 21	**Yes/No Justification**
Junior tennis player aged 17	Veteran male player, aged 53	**Yes/No Justification**

Table 4.16 Individual training needs

ACTION 10

You should be able to explain the principles of rest and recovery, individual needs, progressive overload and specificity from the work you have already done. Either write down or explain to a partner each of these principles. Compare your explanation with your partner's. Are they the same? If they are different, can they both be correct?

E QUESTION

If your body becomes fitter as a result of extra physical work in training, what is likely to happen to your level of fitness if you do less physical work?

Reversibility

You would not willingly apply this principle to your training. It describes what happens to your levels of fitness if you have a break in your training because of an injury, a holiday, because it is the end of the season or because you do not want to train any more. In the same way that your body adapts to an increased level of physical work, it will readapt to a lower level of physical work so you will in effect lose fitness.

FITT principle (Frequency, Intensity, Time, Type)

This is the last of the principles that you need to know. The FITT principle is used to increase the amount of physical work the body does, in other words how you achieve overload. The first three letters in the principle are ways of achieving overload and the fourth letter is a reminder that the overload needs to be specific to the activity for which you are training.

According to this principle, you work harder than before but within your target zone, gradually increasing the amount of work you do.

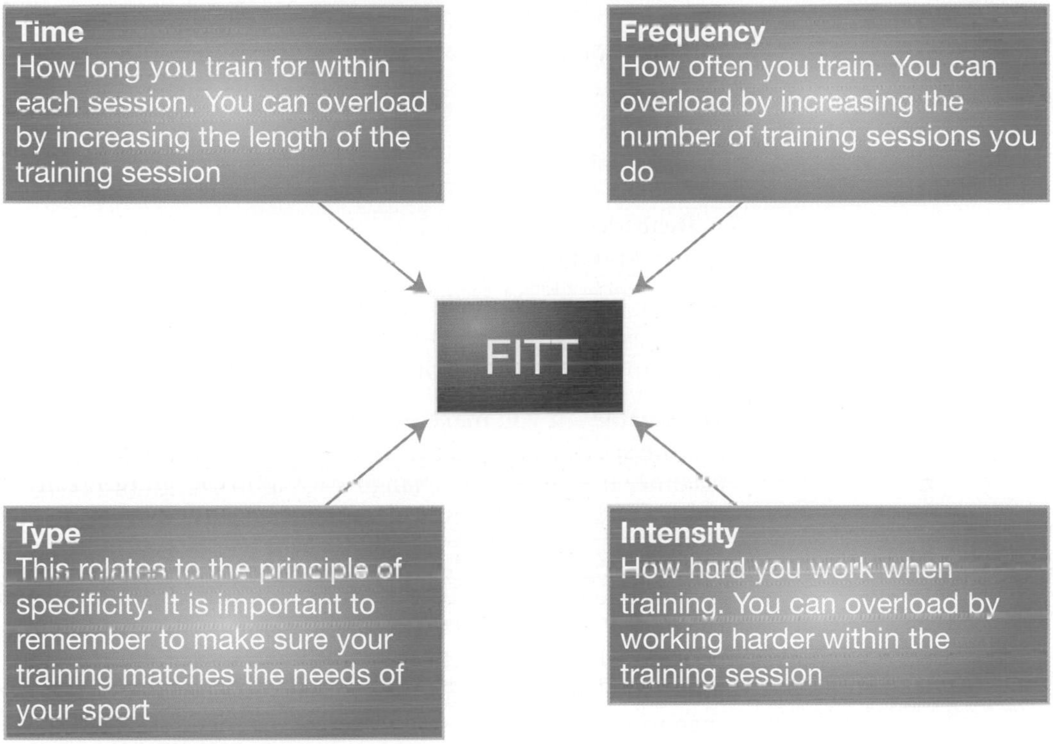

Time
How long you train for within each session. You can overload by increasing the length of the training session
Frequency
How often you train. You can overload by increasing the number of training sessions you do
FITT
Type
This relates to the principle of specificity. It is important to remember to make sure your training matches the needs of your sport
Intensity
How hard you work when training. You can overload by working harder within the training session

Figure 4.3 The components of the FITT Principle

ACTION 11

Your training is different from your friends', some of whom play different sports. This week you trained for an extra session, although last week you made one of the sessions longer than usual. You think that you might work harder within the session next week, but you have said that you will be careful not to do too much because you do not wish to miss any training sessions through injury, as this could lead to a drop in fitness.

Which principles of training are being referred to in this extract?

GOAL SETTING

Goal setting is an important skill to develop – if done properly it can help you in all aspects of your life. It can help you focus on what you want to achieve and give you small steps which ultimately allow you to achieve your overall goal or target.

Goal setting:

- increases attention/focus on what needs to be achieved
- increases motivation/effort (you work harder to achieve the 'goal')
- increases task persistence (helps you stick at something)
- allows you to assess progress over time (are you achieving your goals?)
- can decrease stress (providing you set a manageable goal or target)
- can lead to improved performance (due to the above points).

ACTION 12

In small groups, define, explain and give examples of an application of the principles of training to an activity of your choice.

In order to be effective goal setting needs to follow the SMART principle of goal setting.

SMART principle of goal setting

You need to be able to describe, explain and apply this principle. Each letter of this principle represents a word that needs to be applied to any target or goal that is set:

Specific
Measurable
Achievable
Realistic
Time-bound

Specific – goals need to be clear so that you know exactly what it is you are trying to achieve. A goal of 'getting better in my sport' is not specific – what aspect do you want to improve? How will you know if you have got better?

Measurable – if you make sure the goal is measurable this will automatically make it more specific. You might have an initial goal to improve your sprint time; this becomes measurable by changing it slightly to 'improve my sprint time by one tenth of a second'.. This is measurable because you can tell when it is achieved. Once it is achieved you can set a new target or goal.

Achievable – you could set the following specific and measurable goal: 'increase the height I can jump by 1m.' This goal is not likely to be achievable (an increase of 1m is surely too much?) and although you might try to increase the height you jump, inwardly you would know that the goal is not really attainable and therefore you are likely to give up. Goals therefore need to be realistic.

Realistic – this does not mean easy! If you set yourself a target that is too easy you won't need to try and so you will not improve, but you must make sure the target is achievable as mentioned above. So, the target needs to be challenging to motivate you to work more to achieve it, but not so hard that you give up. This is why goals should really be discussed between the coach and the performer – the performer needs to feel that the goals are realistic. A realistic goal for one performer might be to complete the 100m in 10 seconds, whereas for me it would be nearer 15 seconds!

ACTION 13

Choose one of your practical activities and set yourself a SMART goal. Name the principle of goal setting that you are applying and explain why your goal satisfies this principle.

Time-bound – goals need to have set dates by which they should be achieved. Without this it is too easy to keep putting off the goal: 'I will increase my training sessions from three to four a week' – but when? 'I will reduce my 100m time by 100th of a second' – but when? In order to maintain the motivation to work hard to achieve the goal, clear deadlines have to be given. People will often have short-term goals leading to a long-term goal. For example, some athletes will have a long-term goal of competing in the 2012 Olympic Games; they will also have a series of short-term goals which will focus on aspects of their performance so that they constantly improve leading up to the 2012 Olympics so that they get picked for Team GB and therefore achieve their long-term goal.

PLANNING YOUR PEP

You should now have the basic knowledge required to start planning your PEP. You should plan a PEP as part of your practical work. If your PEP is going to be effective in improving aspects of your health-related exercise it needs to be well thought out and continually evaluated to check you are doing the right things. Development of a PEP should go through the following stages.

Planning

- Check you can increase your activity level safely (PAR-Q).
- Identify your goals (what activity do you want to get fit for?).
- Find out how fit you currently are (carry out some fitness tests).
- Identify your strengths and weaknesses (analyse your fitness test results).
- Select the areas of health-related exercise you need to work on (based on your goals and current weaknesses) and set SMART targets.
- Choose a training method to suit your goal (e.g., continuous training to improve cardiovascular endurance – see Chapter 5).
- Decide on activities and workload to suit your training method.

Performing

- Carry out the PEP sessions.

Evaluating

- Assess the session (could be via re-test).
- Plan the next session (change workload, change activities as appropriate).
- Final testing.
- Final evaluation (did you achieve your goals?).

HOMEWORK

Complete the following activities.

1 Using your list of fitness strengths/weaknesses (based on your fitness test results):
  (a) List the aspects of health-related exercise and skill-related fitness you need to improve.
  (b) Explain how you would use the principles of training to improve these aspects of fitness.

2 Reorganise the following statements/terms to give the correct order of the stages you should go through in order to achieve a planned and effective increase in activity as part of a healthy, active lifestyle.

INCORRECT ORDER:	CORRECT ORDER:
Carry out planned activity	
Complete fitness tests	
Check targets set are SMART targets	
Complete a PAR-Q	
Re-test fitness levels	
Identify targets	
Re-evaluate fitness plan	
Apply the principles of training to develop appropriate fitness plan	

CHAPTER 5 PHYSICAL ACTIVITY AS PART OF YOUR HEALTHY, ACTIVE LIFESTYLE (PART 2)

GOALS

By the end of this chapter you should be able to:
- describe the stages of an exercise session
- explain the difference between aerobic and anaerobic activity
- describe interval, continuous, Fartlek, circuit, weight and cross training
- link methods of training to specific activities
- describe the terms resting heart rate, working heart rate and recovery rates and plot examples on a graph and evaluate results
- graphically demonstrate and explain the use of target zones and training thresholds.

THE EXERCISE SESSION

Any exercise session, whatever the sporting activity, should involve a warm-up before the main activity and a cool-down after it. There are good reasons for this. The warm-up is used to prepare the body for the activity you are about to take part in. It should help you physically and mentally. The cool-down helps return the body to a resting state.

http://www.teachingideas.co.uk:80/pe/contents.htm
Lots of fun warm-up and cool-down ideas.

http://www.tutorials.com/05/0503/0503.asp
Illustrates how to compete some basic stretches and the muscles they stretch.

Warm-up

A proper warm-up has many benefits:

- Muscles which are ready for exercise (through completing a warm-up) will be able to contract and relax more quickly.
- Oxygen will be more easily available to the muscles because of the increased heat of the body.
- It helps the performer to focus on the task they are about to undertake – it is a psychological preparation.

It will also help reduce the risk of injury: you can ensure that muscles and tendons are ready for action by gently increasing the amount of work they do rather than just going from static to very active in one step. Therefore, by using a properly planned warm-up, the performer is less likely to receive a sprain or strain. A warm-up has three phases:

1. Pulse raising/increasing body temperature – this is achieved by completing some form of light continuous activity such as jogging.
2. Stretching, achieved through stretching! You should start from the top and work down, stretching the muscles that will be worked in the main session.
3. Event-specific drills to prepare your body for the activity you are about to do.

Cool-down

Cool-downs do not reduce the risk of injury during performance, but they do reduce the risk of muscle stiffness after performance and speed up the removal of lactic acid (see Chapter 8). They also reduce the risk of fainting after activity by

Figure 5.1 Warming up

keeping the blood circulating back to the heart and gradually reducing the heart rate (see Chapter 7) – the heart rate should be brought down to within 15 bpm of the resting heart rate. Cool-downs have two phases:

1 A reduction in body temperature, slow jogging/walking to bring down the level of activity gradually and help removal of carbon dioxide and lactic acid.

Figure 5.2 Warm up → main activity (competition) → cool down

Aerobic
Working with oxygen.

Anaerobic
Working without oxygen.

2 More stretching to help reduce temperature slowly, to assist in the removal of waste products and to stretch the muscles after they have been working to increase the range of movement possible at the joint.

AEROBIC AND ANAEROBIC ACTIVITY

You need to understand the difference between these two terms so that you can recognise the type of activity you do in your sport. You can then match your training to the requirements of the sport.

In simple terms, aerobic means 'with oxygen', therefore anaerobic means 'without oxygen'. These terms relate to the intensity of the activity, or how hard you are physically making the body work. For example, the 100m sprint is an anaerobic activity because you work as hard as you can (maximal level). When we work at this rate it is not possible to supply the muscles with the oxygen they need to release energy for the exercise, so we work without oxygen, anaerobically, and repay the oxygen debt once the exercise is completed (see Chapter 9). The problem is that because of the lack of oxygen, we can work at this level only for a limited period of time, therefore longer events such as the 3000m are mainly aerobic.

An extreme example of an anaerobic activity is the 100m sprint. An extreme example of an aerobic activity is the marathon, although aspects of the marathon will be anaerobic, e.g., the sprint finish. Similarly, many team games will have aspects of aerobic and anaerobic activity within them.

More information on aerobic and anaerobic respiration can be found in Chapter 9.

E QUESTION

If it takes an elite male 100m runner approximately ten seconds to run the 100m, how long would it take an elite 3000m runner to complete their event if they were able to work at the same anaerobic pace as the 100m runner for the whole race? (See Table 5.1.)

EVENT	PREDICTED TIME FOR EVENT IF SAME PACE COULD BE MAINTAINED ANAEROBICALLY THROUGHOUT THE EVENT
100m	10 seconds
200m	20 seconds
400m	40 seconds
800m	1 minute 20 seconds
1500m	2 minutes 30 seconds
3000m	????

Table 5.1 Applying anaerobic rates

E QUESTION

Read Table 5.2. When do the events appear to change from anaerobic to aerobic?

EVENT	PREDICTED TIME FOR EVENT IF SAME PACE COULD BE MAINTAINED ANAEROBICALLY THROUGHOUT THE EVENT	CURRENT WORLD RECORD (TO NEAREST SECOND)
100m	10 seconds	10 seconds
200m	20 seconds	19 seconds
400m	40 seconds	43 seconds
800m	1 minutes 20 seconds	1 minute 41 seconds
1500m	2 minutes 30 seconds	3 minutes 26 seconds
3000m	????	7 minutes 21 seconds

Table 5.2 From anaerobic to aerobic

E QUESTION

Why do you think you might need a break in your training session? How hard would you be working? Is this aerobic or anaerobic work?

E QUESTION

What was the name of the principle of training which stated that you should match your training to the needs of your sport?

ACTION 1

Copy and complete Table 5.3 by selecting the component of fitness you want to improve to make yourself a better performer.

E QUESTION

Is your sporting activity or your role within it mainly aerobic, anaerobic or a combination of both? The intensity at which you have to work should make a difference to the training method you select.

METHODS OF TRAINING

In the previous chapter you covered the principles of training. Once you understand these principles you will be in a better position to develop an appropriate training programme (PEP) to improve your fitness and therefore your performance in your chosen activity. This means that before preparing your PEP, you need to look at the demands of your sport carefully to see which of the components of fitness are most important.

Now that you have a clearer idea about which aspect of fitness you need to improve, you need to choose a method of training which will bring those improvements. There are several different types of training methods. For this course you need to be able to describe the following methods and give examples of when they would be used:

- continuous training
- interval training
- circuit training
- weight training
- cross training
- Fartlek training.

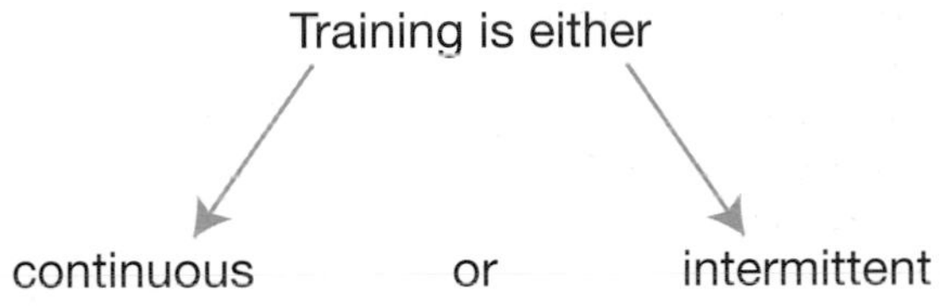

Figure 5.3 Types of training methods

In other words, you are either training without a break (continuously) or training with breaks during the session (intermittently). All of the other types of training fall under one of these headings.

SPORTING ACTIVITY:		
COMPONENT OF HEALTH-RELATED EXERCISE/SKILL-RELATED FITNESS (SEE CHAPTER 3).	IS THIS COMPONENT RELEVANT TO MY SPORTING ACTIVITY?	WHY IS THIS COMPONENT RELEVANT TO MY SPORTING ACTIVITY?
Cardiovascular fitness		
Muscular strength		
Muscular endurance		
Flexibility		
Body composition		
Speed		
Agility		
Balance		
Coordination		
Reaction time		
Power		

Table 5.3 Improving components of fitness

Continuous training

This develops cardiovascular fitness and muscular endurance. As mentioned above, it is called continuous because you do not rest. It is an aerobic activity which uses large muscle groups; activities include cycling, jogging and step aerobics. Continuous training requires the performer to work between 60 and 80 per cent of their training threshold (see thresholds of training later in the chapter), preferably for a minimum of 30 minutes five times a week to have a positive effect on cardiovascular fitness and muscular endurance.

Circuit training

The principles of circuit training are as follows:

1 A number of different exercises are carried out at 'stations'.
2 Each exercise should be carefully selected to make sure that it is relevant to the aim or purpose of the sports performer's PEP. For example, if the performer were a games player and they wanted to improve their muscular endurance, they would include exercises that related to their sport and this area of fitness.
3 The stations are normally positioned in a circular order and are completed one after the other.
4 Care has to be taken to organise the circuit so that different muscle groups are used from one station to the next (to allow the muscles to recover between stations).
5 The performer will work on the station for a set number of repetitions or for a set time before moving on to the next station.
6 You can vary how hard a performer works by adjusting:
   (a) the length of time on each station/number of repetitions at each station
   (b) the number of times the performer must complete the circuit within one training session
   (c) the number of times the performer must complete the circuit training session per week
   (d) the amount of recovery time you allow between each station/complete circuit.

E QUESTION

Which principle of training is being applied by increasing the intensity of the exercise gradually? Match each of the points (a) – (d) to the FITT principle (see Chapter 4).

Figure 5.4 Set up for circuit training session

Circuit training can be used to improve any component of fitness (including skill aspects related to a specific sporting activity), as the exercises and the order in which they are completed can be adapted to suit many needs. For example, as a form of continuous exercise circuit training can improve cardiovascular fitness. By working on specific groups of muscles at several stations, it can also increase muscular endurance. Strength could also be worked on by including weight-bearing exercises (such as press-ups, tricep dips and bench presses using a bench to add resistance) and skills such as passing, shooting and dribbling can be included to improve relevant skill-related aspects of fitness such as agility and coordination.

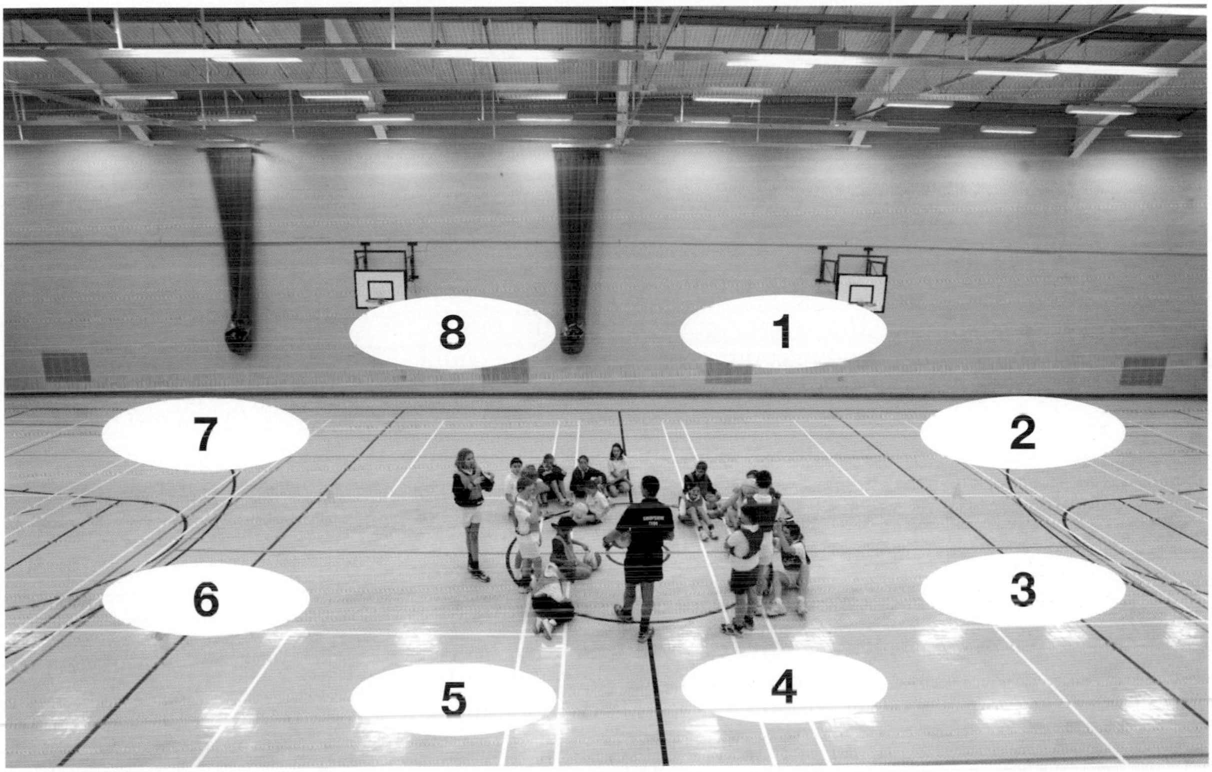

Figure 5.5 Fitness circuit

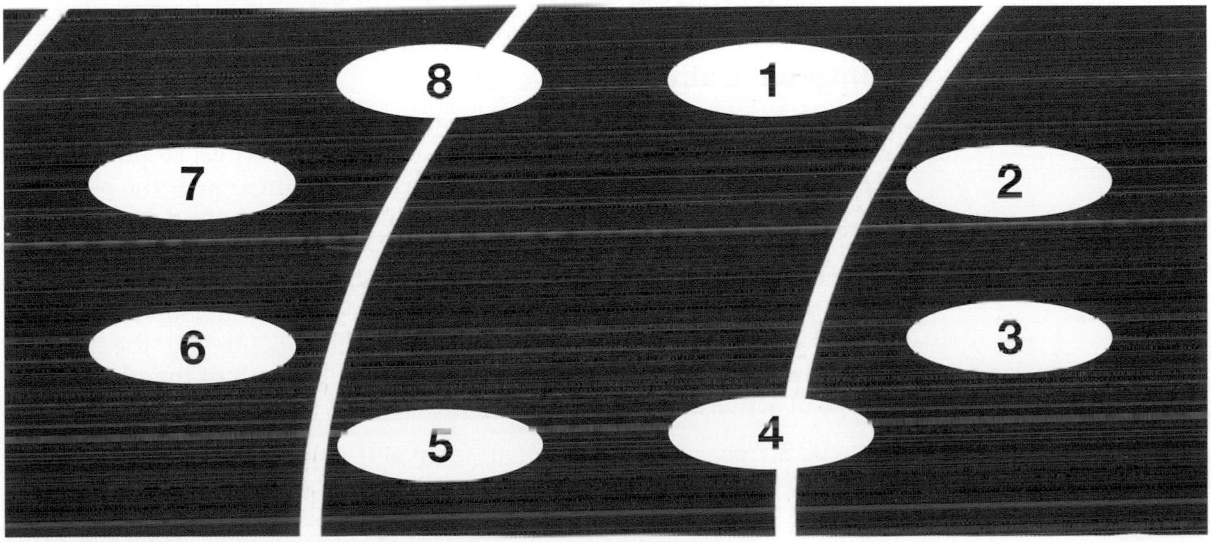

Figure 5.6 Skills circuit

ACTION 2

Figures 5.5 and 5.6 show two different facilities where circuit training can take place. Figure 5.5 will be used for a fitness-related circuit, Figure 5.6 for a skills-related circuit. Each station from the circuit is represented by a number. Choose appropriate activities from Table 5.4 to replace the numbers for each circuit. Make sure you consider the order in which the activities are placed. Add a further three activities to complete the circuits.

Straight dribble	Press-up	Skipping
Chest pass (against the wall)	Sit-up	Tricep dip
Zigzag dribble	Shuttle run	Bench astride
Shooting		

Table 5.4 Activities of circuit training

Fartlek training

This is another form of continuous training. It involves running at different paces and over different terrains. For example, rather than road running at a constant pace, you might increase your speed for 50m and then jog until you have sufficiently recovered before sprinting again. You could run 'off road' through woodland, changing your pace as you go up and down hill. It is a very good training method for games players as it can be tailored to match the demands of the game, i.e., mixing spells of relative inactivity (jogging) with intense activity (sprinting).

Cross training

Cross training combines two or more different types of exercise. Performers whose activities demand a wide range of fitness may use this training method, e.g., tri-athletes or decathletes. A tri-athlete may run in one training session, swim in another, cycle during the third and lift weights in their fourth training session, all within one week. This type of training allows the performer to train all of the required areas of fitness for their activity. Another advantage to cross training is that it provides variety which can help the psychological side to the recovery process provided it is part of a planned training programme.

Interval training

Interval training is a form of intermittent training. Breaks are built into the training session in order to allow the performer to recover so that they can continue to work at high levels of intensity. The 'interval' is the period when they reduce the amount of work they are doing to allow recovery. Due to the use of intervals, this type of training is normally considered for high-intensity work. Sprinters, swimmers and cyclists typically use this type of training, although it can be adapted to suit almost any activity by altering the duration of the work interval, how hard the performer works in the work interval, the number of repetitions within a set, the number of sets, the length of the rest interval and the type of activity carried out during the rest.

Figure 5.7 gives an example of an interval training session.

E QUESTION

Would the following interval training sessions be for a performer preparing for an aerobic or an anaerobic activity?

- 5 × 10 × 50 metres W:R 1:3 Aerobic/anaerobic?
- 5 × 1 × 3000 metres W:R 1:½ Aerobic/anaerobic?

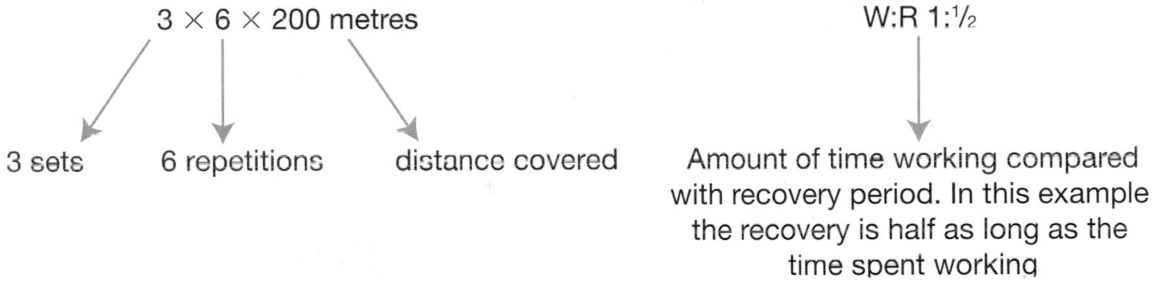

Figure 5.7 Examples of interval training session

E QUESTION

Which training method would be most appropriate to you given your activity, your role within it and your individual needs?

Weight training

Weight training is a form of strength training. You can use free weights (weights that are not attached to machines, such as dumb bells) or weights that are part of a gym machine. You can train to improve muscular strength or muscular endurance. If you chose to increase muscular endurance you would need to lift the weights repeatedly for a number of repetitions and a number of sets. The general standard is 12–20 repetitions per set, for three sets. The weight you use should be light enough to allow you to complete the sets. Strength training, however, requires fewer repetitions and sets but heavier weights. Performers requiring power (e.g., sprinters and field athletes competing in throwing events) would design their weight training so that they increased their strength, whereas performers who rely heavily on muscular endurance (e.g., middle- to long-distance runners and racket players) would design their programme to increase their muscular endurance.

Figure 5.8 Free weights

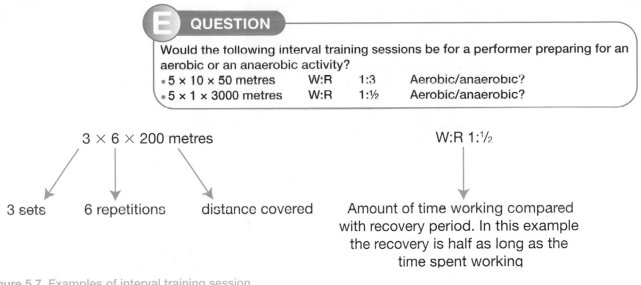

Figure 5.9 Machine-based weights

ACTION 3

Match the images in Figure 5.10 to the training methods discussed.

(a) (b) (c) (d) (e) (f)

Figure 5.10 Which type of training method is represented in each image?

(a) (b) (c) (d) (e)

Figure 5.11 Matching a location to its method of training

E QUESTION

What type of training could you do at the locations in Figure 5.11?

ACTION 4

Match the performers in Figure 5.12 to the most relevant training method.

(a)

(b)

(c)

(d)

(e)

Figure 5.12 Matching the performers to the most relevant training method

When asked to match training methods to types of activity, use the most obvious to ensure you will get a mark.

ACTION 5

Tick each training method in Table 5.5 which you could use to improve each of the components of fitness listed.

	CONTINUOUS	FARTLEK	CIRCUIT	INTERVAL	WEIGHT
Flexibility					
Muscular endurance					
Muscular strength					
Body composition					
Cardiovascular fitness					
Power					
Agility					
Speed					

Table 5.5 Matching training methods with components of fitness

Target zone
This provides the range of heart rate values the performer should work within in order for training intensity to be effective.

TARGET ZONES AND TRAINING THRESHOLDS

It is important to train at the correct intensity for your activity (aerobic or anaerobic) and for yourself (considering your age and current level of fitness). It is suggested that the average performer should train 60–80 per cent of their maximum heart rate, although elite performers will often train outside of this range. The actual percentage that is used to represent maximum and minimum training thresholds will vary depending on the level of the performer and what they are trying to achieve, but the principle explained below remains the same. To help us achieve the correct training intensity we use target training zones.

E QUESTION
What happens to the target zone as the performer gets older?

The top line on the graph in Figure 5.13 represents the maximum heart rate (beats per minute – bpm) values for the age groups specified (15, 20, 25, 30). This value is calculated by taking the performer's age from the base rate of 220 bpm. The middle line represents the **maximum training threshold** (80 per cent of maximum heart rate) and the lower line represents the **minimum training threshold** (60 per cent of maximum heart rate). The area between the minimum and maximum training thresholds is called the **target zone**, i.e., it is the area that you should try to work within so that your body is working hard enough to cause it to adapt but not so hard that the training has a negative effect.

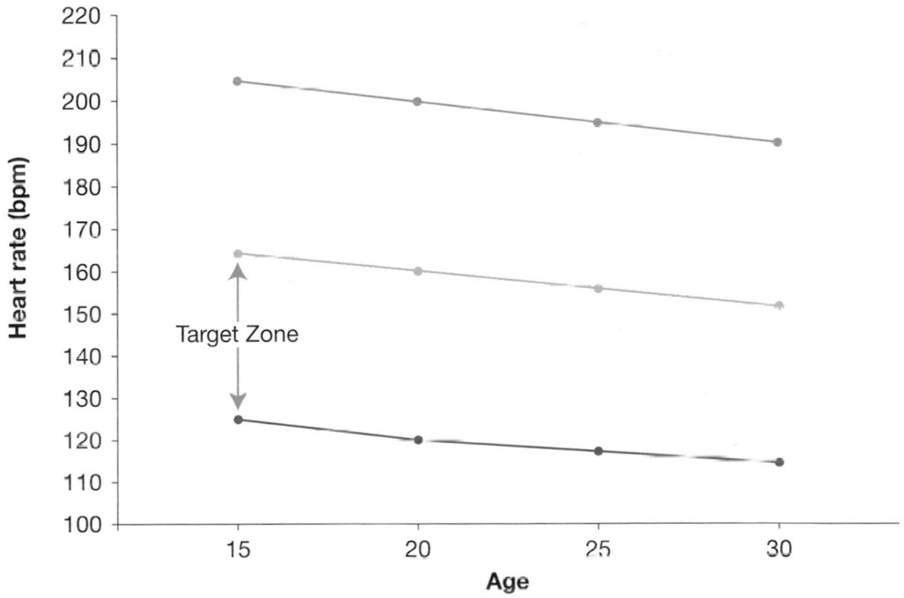

Figure 5.13 Thresholds of training and target zones

E QUESTION

Use the graph in Figure 5.13 to give the target zone heart rates for the following:
- a club swimmer aged 25
- a school tennis player aged 15
- a veteran rugby player aged 30.

E QUESTION

Table 5.6 shows the actual heart rate values used to produce the graph in Figure 5.13.
If maximum heart rate is calculated by subtracting the performer's age from 220, enter the heart rate values for performers aged 45 and 50 and their target zones.

	15	20	25	30	35	40	45	50
Max heart rate (MHR)	205	200	195	190	185	180		
80% MHR	164	160	156	152	148	144		
60% MHR	123	120	117	114	111	108		

Table 5.6 Calculating heart rate values

Exam questions will ask about the immediate effects of exercise, the effects of regular training and the long-term benefits of exercise to the body. It is important to know the difference between these terms.

THE EFFECTS OF EXERCISE

The purpose of training is to become fitter so that the body is able to cope more easily with the physical demands placed upon it. The reason that the body is more able to cope is because it adapts to the training. Your body changes as a result of physical work and these changes are summarised in Chapters 8–11.

Obviously these three areas are linked. We experience the immediate effects of exercise, which if brought into play on a regular basis (through regular exercise) become permanent adaptations (while the level of activity is maintained). These adaptations then bring health benefits.

Recovery rates

One of the immediate effects of exercise is an increase in heart rate. A person's recovery rate is the amount of time it takes for their heart rate to return to its resting rate after they have finished exercising. The reason the heart rate remains high is that it is continuing to deliver an increased amount of oxygen to the muscles (this is called paying back the oxygen debt), to reduce lactic acid content and to transport carbon dioxide to the lungs. The quicker your heart rate returns to its resting value, the fitter you are thought to be.

Recovery rate
This is the amount of time it takes for the heart rate to return to 'normal' resting level after exercise

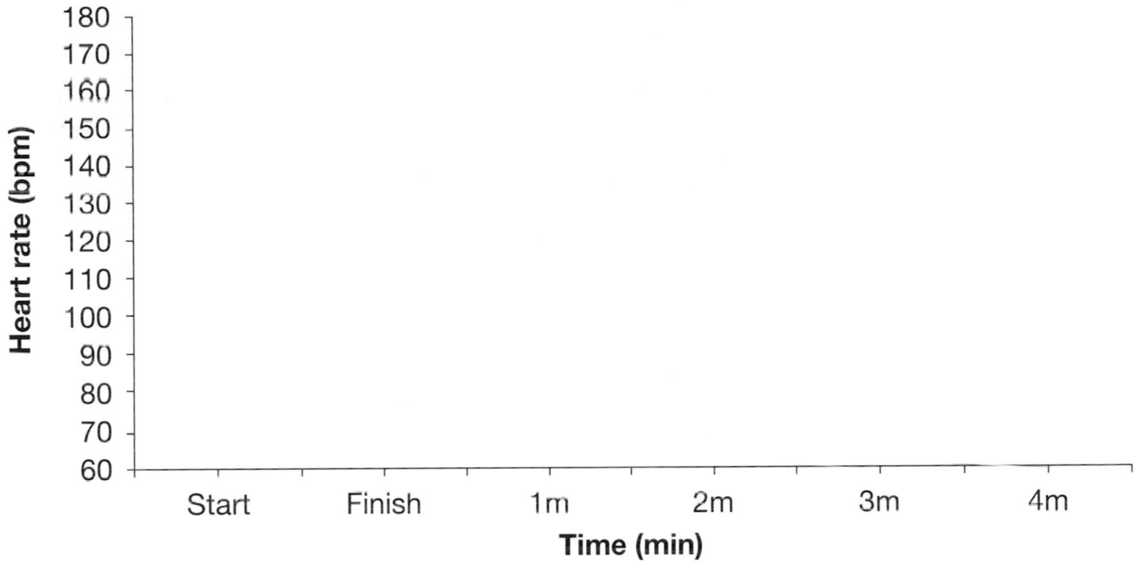

Figure 5.14 Graph showing heart rate values in bpm.

ACTION 6

Take your resting heart rate and plot it on the graph in Figure 5.14. Take part in some aerobic exercise for five minutes. At the end of the exercise, take your heart rate again and plot on the graph. Continue to take your heart rate every minute until it is back to your resting level. Compare your heart rate values with others' in your group. Whose heart rate returned to resting the quickest? Does this mean that that person is the fittest, or is there another reason for the differences in heart rate?

CONSIDERATIONS FOR YOUR PEP

You should use your PEP to demonstrate your understanding of the work you have completed so far. You should consider the following:

- the requirements of the activity (specificity – aerobic? anaerobic?)
- your goal/aim (areas of fitness to improve – individual differences) – do not forget this can be to increase fitness after injury (i.e., as part of a rehabilitation programme)
- which training method will help you achieve your goal/aim
- how you can apply progressive overload
- at what rate you should apply the overload
- the structure of the exercise session (warm-up, main activity, cool-down)
- the possible use of target zones to set training levels
- the possible use of recovery rates to monitor progress.

HOMEWORK

In the previous action, the fitness and skill circuits were kept separate, but they can be combined. Choose a team game and design a suitable circuit for someone who plays that game. Make sure you include activities relevant to the game and to the components of fitness you think are important to that game. Explain your choice of activities within your circuit to others in your class.

CHAPTER 6 YOUR PERSONAL HEALTH AND WELL-BEING

GOALS

By the end of this chapter you should be able to:
- explain the link between exercise, diet, work and rest and their influence on personal health and well-being
- state the requirements of a balanced diet and the role played by the nutrients, fibre and water
- explain why the timing of dietary intake in relation to sporting activity should be considered.

http://www.fitness2live.co.uk/games/eb.html
A fun way to look at the energy equation!

THE LINK BETWEEN EXERCISE, DIET, WORK AND REST

As mentioned in Chapter 1 health refers to the physical, social and mental well-being of an individual. This chapter relates to our diet and how this contributes to our well-being, although more detail can be found in Chapter 7.

Diet is one of the factors that contributes to a healthy lifestyle and general well-being. In order to work physically and mentally we need to provide the body with the nutrients, fibre and water it needs, and to give time for recovery we need to achieve a balance between exercise and work. We can do this with adequate rest and the correct diet. Making the right choices of foods and drinks and taking regular exercise can protect against coronary heart disease and many common cancers and other diseases such as osteoporosis – you can feel better, improve weight control (this is not just about losing weight) and relieve stress.

The more physical work we do, the more energy we need to complete it. Food contains calories, which are used within the body to release energy for physical

Figure 6.1 The energy equation

E QUESTION
Why is it acceptable for some people to eat more than others?

work. Sports performers will use more calories than those who do not exercise and so they can afford to consume more food for energy. Performers must be careful, however, that they do not eat too much, otherwise excess carbohydrates will be stored as fat and provide additional weight. This will mean that they have to work harder every time they exercise because of the extra weight they are carrying. Athletes must ensure that Energy IN = Energy OUT.

A BALANCED DIET

It is very important to eat a balanced diet, whether or not you take part in physical activity. The word diet refers to what you eat, although it is often used to suggest that someone needs to change his or her eating habits. You have probably heard other people say that they need to 'go on a diet' or make reference to specific regimes such as low-fat or low-carbohydrate diets. 'Diet' in all of these cases is being used in a slightly different way. For the purposes of this course you need to think of diet as what you eat and a balanced diet as what you should eat.

Macronutrient Nutrients that are required in large quantities in our diet, e.g. carbohydrates.

A balanced diet is important as it will give you all the nutrients you need to help you keep healthy and to provide the right amount of energy for the physical work that you do. Current health studies show that a healthy balanced diet should contain:

- macronutrients (nutrients required in large quantities):
  - carbohydrates (starchy foods such as bread, potatoes, rice and pasta)
  - fats (dairy products, fatty meat, sweets)
  - protein (found in meat, fish, eggs and beans)

Figure 6.2 The Eatwell Plate
Source: Food Standards Agency

It is not necessary to remember exact percentages of the requirements of the different types of nutrients to give a balanced diet, but you do need to be able to say whether you need 'more or less' of one nutrient compared to another. For example, you should eat less fat than carbohydrate in your diet.

Micronutrients
Nutrients that are required in small quantities in our diet, e.g. minerals.

- micronutrients (nutrients required in small quantities):
  - vitamins (mainly from fresh fruit and vegetables)
  - minerals (found in most foods, particularly vegetables)
- water (found in most food and obviously liquids)
- fibre (found in vegetables, fruits, nuts, cereal).

Most people will eat a mixture of foods but not necessarily in the correct proportions. Figure 6.2 shows the Eatwell Plate produced by the British Nutrition Foundation demonstrating the proportion and types of food suggested to achieve a balanced diet.

Different texts will show slightly different proportions or percentages of foods, but it is important to see from the various available sources of information that:

- macronutrients and micronutrients, water and fibre are represented
- carbohydrates make up the bulk of our diet
- fats should not be removed from the diet completely.

E QUESTION

Can you remember the difference between aerobic and anaerobic activity? Explain it to a partner and ask them to give you an example of each activity type.

ACTION 1

Match the images in Figure 6.3 to the correct food group in Table 6.1 by ticking the appropriate box. (Remember, many foods contain more than one food group.)

If you are asked to give examples of macronutrients found in specific items of food, select the most obvious, for example, meat – protein; potatoes – carbohydrates. Although both of these food items contain different types of nutrients, you will be expected to give the one it contains the most of. Therefore, going for the obvious is a good way to make sure you get the mark!

WHY DO WE NEED THESE FOOD GROUPS?

Carbohydrates are used to provide the body with energy for physical work. They can be used during aerobic or anaerobic activity.

Fats are used to provide the body with energy for physical work and to keep the body warm. They are used in aerobic activity.

Protein is generally used for growth and repair of cells within the body, but can be used as an energy source in extreme circumstances (in other words, when usual energy sources are depleted). Protein is obviously very important to a sports performer as it is used in muscular hypertrophy (an effect of regular training, where the muscle increases in size) and repairing muscle tissue.

Vitamins and minerals are necessary because they help in the formation of the tissues of our body, e.g., hair, skin, nails, teeth and bones. They are also used in chemical reactions in the body and keep us free from disease.

IMAGE:	A	B	C	D	E	F	G	H
FOOD GROUP								
Fats								
Carbohydrates								
Proteins								
Minerals								
Vitamins								
Water								
Fibre								

Table 6.1 Foods and food groups

Fibre is an essential aid to digestion. It is not digested by the body but slowly makes its way through our digestive system before being expelled with other unwanted substances. It reduces the chances of suffering from bowel cancer.

Water is essential in our diet, although it is not a nutrient. It prevents us from becoming dehydrated and helps to regulate body temperature. During periods of exercise we should make sure we drink more water than we do at rest to replace the water lost through sweating.

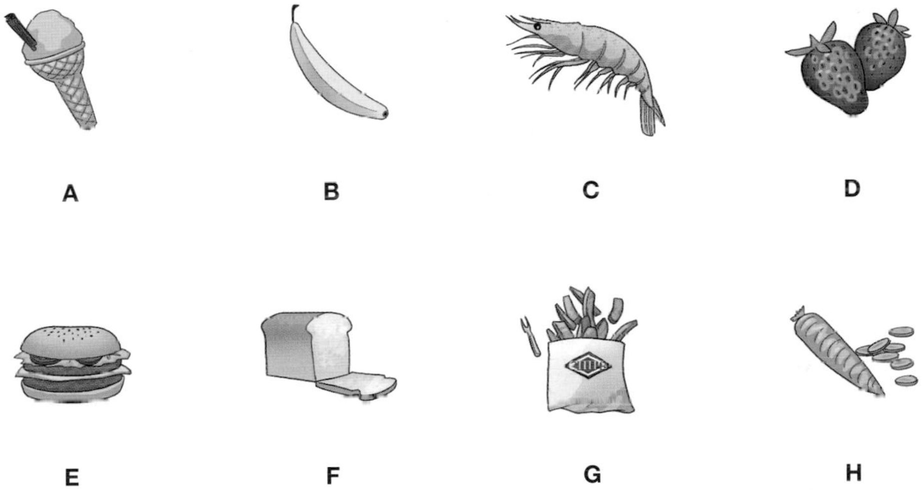

Figure 6.3 Match the foods shown to the correct food group

ACTION 2

Write a list of what you have eaten today or yesterday. Copy Table 6.1, but this time tick the food groups to represent what you have eaten. Every time one of the food groups is represented in something you have eaten (such as fat), make sure you add an extra tick. How many ticks do you have in each column? Have you had a balanced diet?

ACTION 3

Complete the statements in Figure 6.4 about diet.

Carbohydrates are the main source of ______ for a performer, but they may also gain energy from ______ and ______. ______ are also used for growth and repair of tissue so play an important role if the performer has suffered an ______. Dehydration results if insufficient ______ is consumed before, during or after an activity. Fibre is important in maintaining healthy ______ movement. ______ and ______ are the remaining components of a balanced diet, they are essential to the help in the formation of ______ and for ______ reactions in the body.

Figure 6.4 Roles of the components of a balanced diet

E QUESTION

1 If we eat more calories than we use, what do you think the outcome will be?
2 If we eat fewer calories than we need, what do you think the outcome will be?

TIMING OF DIETARY INTAKE

Although we need macronutrients for energy it is important that we do not eat a substantial meal just prior to exercise (a two-hour minimum time gap between eating and exercise is recommended). In order to understand why, we need to know a little about the circulatory system. When we are resting a large percentage of the blood circulating the body is directed to the liver and kidneys so that digestive functions can be carried out. Although blood is still flowing to all parts of the body the amount available for the skeletal muscles (the muscles we use for physical activity) is reduced. This isn't a problem whilst at rest because there is still sufficient blood to transport the required oxygen to the muscles (the muscles use less oxygen when at rest than when exercising). A problem arises if we need to exercise because if blood flow remained the same there would not be enough oxygen delivered. To overcome this problem blood is redistributed to the muscles.

When we exercise blood is redistributed so that a greater percentage of it (from 20 per cent to 80 per cent) flows to the skeletal muscles (this is so that it can provide oxygen and remove carbon dioxide so the muscles can continue to function when we ask them to work harder). If more blood is flowing to the muscles, less is available for the digestive system (from 45 per cent to 2 per cent). This can result in very uncomfortable stomach cramps and a drop in performance.

There are three terms you will need to remember:

- shunting – this is the term given to the process which results in the redistribution of blood flow
- vasodilation – this is the relaxation of the muscular wall in the blood vessel (arteriole) so that the internal diameter of the blood vessel becomes wider so more blood can flow through (the actual vessel doesn't become bigger, just the space within it that allows more blood to pass through)
- vasoconstriction – this is the opposite to vasodilation. It means the arteriole has contracted so that less blood can flow through the vessel.

✓ Redistribution of blood flow
Vasoconstriction or vasodilation of blood vessels to alter rate of blood flow through them to control quantities of blood going to different parts of the body.

Vasoconstriction
Contraction of the muscular wall of the arteriole to reduce blood flow through the vessel.

Vasodilation
Relation of the muscular wall of the arteriole to increase blood flow through the vessel.

ACTION 4

Look at the two images of the blood vessel in Figure 6.5.

1 Which blood vessel, A or B, is vasodilated?
2 Which blood vessel A, or B, is vasoconstricted?
3 What has happened to the blood flow in vessel B compared with that in vessel A?
4 Which blood vessel, A or B, represents a blood vessel in skeletal muscle during exercise? Explain your answer.

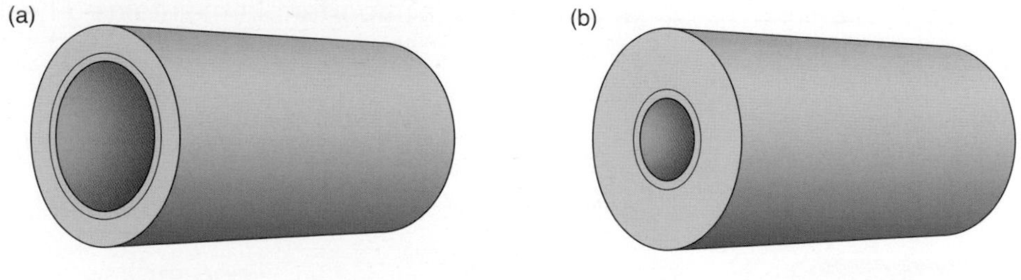

Figure 6.5 Blood flow

SECTION 2

YOUR HEALTHY, ACTIVE BODY

YOUR HEALTHY, ACTIVE BODY

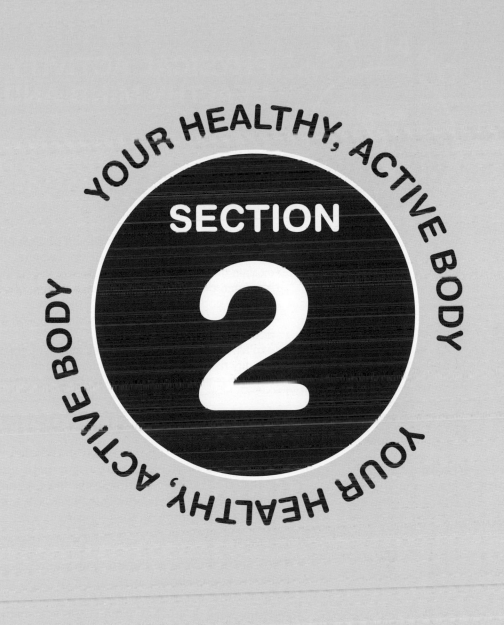

CHAPTER 7

PHYSICAL ACTIVITY AND YOUR HEALTHY MIND AND BODY

GOALS

By the end of this chapter you should be able to:
- state the variables affecting optimum weight
- explain the terms obese, overfat, overweight, underweight, anorexic
- state and describe the extreme categories of somatotyping and link each extreme body type to physical activity
- explain the effects of smoking and alcohol on general health and physcial activity
- explain the potential advantages and dangers of drug use in sport
- identify risks associated with physical activity and how to reduce these risks.

Optimum weight
Being at the right weight for you, considering all the variables that can impact on weight, such as age, height, build, physical activity.

VARIABLES AFFECTING OPTIMUM WEIGHT

Guidelines are given by government health departments about people's optimum weight (the best weight for you). These charts suggest whether someone is overweight or not by considering age, height and gender. It is important to remember that these are only guidelines as optimum weight varies between individuals depending on the following factors.

Gender

There are differences in the structure and physiology of men's and women's bodies (you probably knew that!). On average, men have more muscle mass than women, although there are always exceptions. So even if a man and a woman were the same height, you would expect the man to weigh more than the woman due to the increased weight of their muscle. Because of this, men have an advantage over women in strength events, which is one of the reasons why men and women do not normally compete against each other in activities relying heavily on strength.

Height

The taller you are, the more you would be expected to weigh, therefore in some events it is helpful to be short because you will weigh less. For example, jockeys are normally very small and try to keep their weight as low as possible. Why do you think they need to do this?

Bone structure

Bone also weighs heavily. Some people have a bigger bone structure than others and so will weigh more. This could be an advantage in contact sports where bone strength is important to withstand physical contact.

Muscle girth

This is the size or circumference of the muscle. A larger circumference implies larger muscles, which explains why someone with large muscles may weigh more than the expected standard.

Being the 'correct weight' is important in most sports, but particularly important in the following activities. Do you know why?

- horse-racing
- gymnastics
- boxing.

Elite sports performers pay a lot of attention to their diet to make sure it is correct for their activity. The performers listed in Table 7.1 are all clearly the correct weight for their activities, but how does their weight compare with the 'expected' weight for their age and height using standard tables?

PERFORMER	M/F	ACTIVITY	HEIGHT (CM)	GUIDELINE WEIGHT (KG) BASED ON AGE AND HEIGHT	APPROXIMATE WEIGHT (KG)
Franki Detorri	M	Jockey	162.6	59	53
Paula Radcliffe	F	Long distance runnor	172.7	63.5	54
David Beckham	M	Football	182.9	80.7	75.7
Jonah Lomu	M	Rugby	195.6	94.3	125
Martin Johnson	M	Rugby	200.7	99.8	119

Table 7.1 Comparing guidelines with sport requirements

ACTION 1

Look at the information in Table 7.1.

- Which performer is the shortest? What activity do they participate in?
- Consider the approximate weight and guideline weight for each of the performers. What do you notice? If the weight is more than that recommended, what might be causing the extra weight? If the weight is under that expected, why might this be the case?
- Can you see any link between weight and activity? Why are these performers considered to be the correct weight for what they do?
- What does this tell you about using standardised tables to judge whether you are overweight or underweight?

Research

The government is so concerned about the health of the nation that it has set up areas of research. For example the National Child Measurement Programme (NCMP) weighs and measures children aged 4–5 years and 10–11 years. The findings from 2007–2008 are shown.

		UNDERWEIGHT	HEALTHY WEIGHT	OVERWEIGHT	OBESE	OVERWEIGHT AND OBESE COMBINED	NUMBER MEASURED
4–5 year olds	Boys	1.5%	74.5%	13.6%	10.4%	24.0%	244,587
	Girls	1.0%	77.9%	12.3%	8.8%	21.1%	233,065
	Both	1.3%	76.2%	13.0%	9.6%	22.6%	477,652
10–11 year olds	Boys	1.2%	64.5%	14.4%	21.0%	34.3%	255,302
	Girls	1.6%	67.6%	14.2%	16.6%	30.7%	240,119
	Both	1.4%	66.0%	14.3%	18.3%	32.6%	495,421

Table 7.2

Source: http://www.ic.nhs.uk/webfiles/publications/ncmp/ncmp0708/NCMP%202007-08%20Report.pdf

QUESTION

Which is the heaviest group in terms of weight in Table 7.2?

QUESTION

Look at the number of young people in Table 7.2 who do not have a healthy weight. Does this surprise you? What should we be doing about this?

QUESTION

Why are the government measuring those underweight as well as overweight?

QUESTION

What can individuals do to control their weight (in terms of being underweight as well as overweight)?

Obese
A potentially harmful condition where a person has a abnormally high proportion of body fat.

Anorexia nervosa
An eating disorder where an individual believes that they need to lose weight even though they are already underweight; can lead to hospitalisation or even death.

Obese

Obese is a term used to describe people who are very overfat.

It refers to the person having an abnormally high proportion of body fat in their bodies. This is a potentially harmful condition due to the additional strain it places on the body's systems and can damage your helath. There are medical syndromes or gentic disorders that can cause obesity but the majority of people who are obese are thought to be so due to either a poor diet, lack of exercise, or both.

Overfat

This term is a way of saying that you have more body fat than you should have.

Overweight

This is a term used to describe people who 'have weight in excess of normal'. This judgement is based on expected weight for people's height, age and sex. This excess weight may be caused by fat, but it could also be due to muscle, bone and/or water content of the body; e.g. a bodybuilder with limited fat content could still be overweight, due to the amount of muscle.

Underweight

Underweight is a term used to describe people who do not have the recommended amount of body fat in relation to their age and height.

Anorexia nervosa

This is an eating disorder brought about through a distorted impression of self image and low self-esteem. In other words someone who clearly does not need to lose weight believes themselves to be fat and so voluntarily 'starves' in an attempt to lose the weight they think they need to make themselves attractive. The problem is because they have a distorted impression of how they really look they are starving the body of essential nutrients and seriously damaging their health. This condition (if left unchecked) will result in hospitalisation or death. According to a national charity that focuses on eating disorders – *beat* (see http://www.b-eat.co.uk/) – only about 40 per cent of those suffering with anorexia nervosa will make a complete recovery. The condition mainly affects females between the age of 15 and 19, but males also suffer with this condition. Approximately one per cent of 16 to 18 year olds have anorexia. Table 7.3 shows the increasing cases of anorexia nervosa that were diagnosed and admitted to English NHS hospitals between 1996 and 2006.

	ANOREXIA
2005–06	620
2004–05	517
2003–04	532
2002–03	552
2001–02	497
2000–01	469
1999–2000	482
1998–99	465
1997–98	484
1996–97	419

Table 7.3

Source: http://www.disordered-eating.co.uk/eating-disorders-statistics/anorexia-nervosa-statistics-uk.html

SOMATOTYPING

William Sheldon described three general body types. He called them:

- ectomorph
- mesomorph
- endomorph.

Ectomorphs

Ectomorphs' characteristics are:

- tall and thin (skeletal height is the most important measurement)
- delicate build
- lightly muscled
- suitable body type for endurance activities.

Mesomorphs

Mesomorphs' characteristics are:

- muscular or athletic build (width of the shoulders is the most important measurement)
- gain muscle relatively easily
- add little fat
- built for physical activity involving speed and/or strength and/or power.

Endomorphs

Endomorphs' characteristics are:

- larger individuals with a rounded appearance (the width of the hips is the most important measurement)
- have trouble losing weight
- can gain muscle
- only suited to specific sports that do not require speed or mobility due to additional weight.

These general body types are extreme, i.e. very few people are completely endomorph, mesomorph or ectomorph.

ECTOMORPH
Narrow shoulders and narrow hips
MESOMORPH
Wide shoulders and narrow hips
ENDOMORPH
Wide hips and narrow shoulders

Figure 7.1 Classic body types

ACTION 2

Find some images of elite track athletes (newspapers or the internet are potentially good sources). Make a collage of the athletes to display on the wall. Look at their body composition. You should notice that it is difficult to see any additional fat stores under their skin regardless of whether they are a sprinter, middle- distance or long-distance runner. These athletes are achieving the correct energy balance for their events. Do all elite track and field athletes have the same physique? If not, why do you think this is?

E QUESTION

Why would the government support the banning of smoking in public places?

HOMEWORK

Find as many pictures of elite performers from as many different sporting events as you can, and combine them with someone else's from your group. Organise the images into groups based on the body types of the performers, not by activity.

- Do any of the groups of images fall into Sheldon's three categories?
- If so, which categories are represented?
- Even though you did not sort the images on sporting activity, do the images within each group tend to be from the same type of activity anyway?
- What does this tell you about the required body type for that activity?
- Are any of Sheldon's body types not represented? What does this tell you about the suitability of that body type for physical activity?

THE EFFECTS OF SMOKING AND ALCOHOL ON HEALTH AND PERFORMANCE

Smoking

In Chapters 8 and 9 we looked at some of the effects of smoking and alcohol on the cardiovascular and respiratory systems in particular. This section gives some more general information. A major breakthrough to protect people from passive smoking or secondhand smoking was made when smoking in public places was banned in England from the 1 July 2007.

Figure 7.2 Ban on smoking in public places

The desire for these bans is based on growing evidence that passive smoking as well as active smoking is harmful to our health, leading to heart and lung disease, cancer and premature death.

- If you smoke, you are two to three times more likely to have a heart attack than a non-smoker, and much more likely to die from heart disease. Smokers are also more likely to have strokes, blood clots, and angina.
- Tobacco smoking can result in respiratory diseases like emphysema and chronic bronchitis, and leaves sufferers breathless and unable to do much activity.
- As a smoker, your risk of developing diabetes in adult life is two to three times higher than that of a non-smoker.
- Tobacco contains nicotine, which is addictive. This is why giving up smoking is so difficult, even though people know the risks of continuing.

Apart from the obvious health risks, smoking will decrease performance in practical activity due to the carbon monoxide contained in cigarette smoke. The haemoglobin in the red blood cells that is normally used to carry oxygen will carry carbon monoxide in preference, reducing the amount of oxygen available to release energy and the performer's ability to work aerobically. Heavy smokers may have as much as ten per cent of their haemoglobin bound by carbon monoxide. This obviously has more of an effect on performers in endurance events, but will affect the recovery of all performers.

Alcohol

Figure 7.3 Some young people drink alcohol to be sociable

Many people drink moderate amounts of alcohol to be sociable. The immediate effects of alcohol vary depending on the amount consumed, and therefore the amount of alcohol in the blood. If low amounts of alcohol are consumed you can witness the following effects:

- relaxes the drinker
- reduces tension
- lowers inhibitions
- impairs concentration
- slows reflexes
- impairs reaction time
- reduces coordination
- causes loss of balance.

While the first two bullet points might release stress, the last five points will have a negative impact on performance. As a result, alcohol should not be drunk before sporting activity. Like nicotine, alcohol can become addictive.

Long-term effects of drinking too much alcohol include:

- increased weight (due to the calories in alcohol)
- cancer of the liver and/or bowel
- heart failure
- high blood pressure.

ACTION 3

Choose a sporting activity and complete Table 7.4 by giving an example of how the stated effects of alcohol would affect a performer in the chosen activity.

EFFECT OF ALCOHOL	EXAMPLE OF HOW PERFORMANCE IS AFFECTED
Impairs concentration	
Slows reflexes	
Impairs reaction time	
Reduces co-ordination	
Loss of balance	
Increased weight	

Table 7.4 Effects of alcohol on physical activity

E QUESTION

Why are elite athletes under so much pressure to find ways to improve performance?

PERFORMANCE-ENHANCING DRUGS

Elite performers dedicate their lives to becoming as good as they can possibly be, and hopefully the best in their chosen activity. They are under huge amounts of pressure to find ways to increase their performance, and for some the pressure is so great that they turn to performance-enhancing drugs – i.e. drugs that will help them perform to an even higher standard in their sport.

DRUG TYPE/ CLASS	EXAMPLES	POSSIBLE WAYS TO ENHANCE PERFORMANCE	EXAMPLE OF HARMFUL SIDE EFFECTS
Stimulants	Amphetamines Caffeine	Increase in physical/mental alertness Increased confidence Increased metabolic rate	Aggression Anxiety Insomnia Irregular and increased heart rate
Narcotic analgesics	Methadone Morphine Codeine	Reduce pain felt, therefore 'hides' injury	Nausea and vomiting Loss of concentration Loss of balance/ coordination May lead to permanent injury Addiction
Anabolic steroids	Testosterone Nandrolone	Train harder for longer, therefore increase strength/power	Liver/kidney damage Aggression Premature heart disease Acne Low sperm count
Diuretics	Bendrofluazide	Quick weight loss, therefore can 'make weight' for specific weight category Urine passed sooner, therefore if other drugs taken 'evidence' is passed out of the body sooner	Dehydration Nausea Kidney/liver failure
Beta blockers	Atenolol Propranolol	Calm and relaxing effect	Tiredness Low blood pressure
Peptide hormones	EPO (erythopoietin) HGH (human growth hormone)	EPO Increases red blood cell count, therefore increases the oxygen-carrying capacity of the blood HGH increases muscle size	EPO Increased viscosity (thickness/stickiness) therefore increased risk of heart failure

Table 7.5 Effects of drugs on the body

The problem with this is that the use of performance-enhancing drugs is banned and considered to be cheating, so anyone found taking drugs would be disqualified. The two main reasons they are banned are:

1 they artificially improve your performance, so if you take them you are cheating
2 taking the drugs may improve performance, but they also present dangerous side effects, which the athletes should be protected from.

Table 7.5 summarises the drugs you should be aware of, the advantages to the performer and some of their harmful side effects. You will not be exepcted to know actual examples of drugs, but you do need to know the type (class) of drug, why performers might take them and the potentially damaging side effects.

ACTION 4

Research the most recent major sporting championships (e.g. Beijing 2008 Olympic Games, the World Swimming Championships, Road Cycling World Championships, World Indoor Athletics Championships, or the World Weightlifting Championships). Try to find further examples of reports of performers who have failed drugs tests and therefore are accused of taking performance-enhancing drugs. Add their details to Table 7.6. Consider the performers in column 1, their sport and the drug they were accused of taking; complete column 4 by giving an example of a way in which their performance may benefit by taking this drug, then complete column 5 by giving a harmful side effect that they may experience as a result.

PERFORMER 1	SPORTING ACTIVITY 2	DRUG ACCUSED OF TAKING 3	HOW WOULD IT IMPROVE THEIR PERFORMANCE? 4	POSSIBLE HARMFUL SIDE EFFECTS OF THIS TYPE OF DRUG 5
Fani Halkia	Hurdles (2008 Summer Olympics)	Anabolic Steroids		
Moises Duenas Nevado	Cycling (2008 Tour De France)	EPO		
John George	MMA Fighter (mixed martial arts – 2008)	Anabolic Steroids		
Ouyang Kunpeng	Swimming	Anabolic steroids		
Kieren Fallon	Horse racing (2007)	Stimulant		
Frankie Dettori	Horse racing (1999)	Diuretics		

Table 7.6 Performers who have failed drugs tests

ACTION 5

Complete the word search on the handout provided by your teacher to find the names of performance-enhancing drugs AND some possible side effects. The words you are looking for are given in Table 7.7.

PERFORMANCE-ENHANCING DRUGS WORD SEARCH

S	A	D	V	U	Q	U	J	A	E	T	O	C	O	G
G	R	L	K	R	D	P	W	R	L	J	Q	W	O	N
W	U	E	E	R	J	I	Z	E	Y	X	W	K	C	I
K	R	J	K	R	O	C	U	D	T	R	A	I	N	P
H	R	X	Z	C	T	Y	X	R	T	M	S	O	S	O
N	E	G	Y	X	O	E	S	A	E	R	C	N	I	D
U	D	B	D	E	L	L	Y	H	E	T	C	P	J	D
U	U	W	T	V	S	P	B	L	J	V	I	I	Z	O
S	C	S	T	I	M	U	L	A	N	T	S	C	R	O
E	T	A	L	U	M	I	T	S	T	Q	U	E	S	L
C	I	U	E	C	K	S	U	H	Z	E	G	M	O	B
S	O	F	G	N	F	D	Z	V	G	N	B	X	P	Z
B	N	Y	I	T	G	O	W	B	O	I	H	P	J	V
K	E	A	E	F	G	C	G	L	O	Q	E	S	G	G
S	P	N	G	J	C	E	S	Z	T	Y	N	W	M	N

Train	Painkiller	Stimulants
Diuretics	Beta blockers	Stimulate
Alert	CNS	Longer
Harder	Increase oxygen	Blood doping

Table 7.7 Drugs and their side effects

ACTION 6

Use the words you find in the word search (or Table 7.7) to complete Table 7.8 by matching the drug type with its effects.

Add an extra column to Table 7.8, giving an example of a sporting activity often associated with the illegal drug, due to the way the drug may enhance performance.

http://www.uksport.gov.uk/drugs/
Gives actual drugs testing results from UK sport.

DRUG TYPE	HOW IT ENHANCES PERFORMANCE
Anabolic Steroids	Reduction in central nervous system activity
Narcotic Analgesics	Weight loss/mask the presence of other drugs

Table 7.8 How drugs can enhance performance

RISKS ASSOCIATED WITH PHYSICAL ACTIVITY AND HOW TO REDUCE THESE RISKS

The term sports injury refers to the kinds of injuries that commonly occur during sport or exercise. As we know physical activity can be very beneficial to health as it reduces the risk of heart disease, stroke and obesity and helps to beat depression.

However, exercise can also cause injuries, particularly if you do not prepare properly, use the proper safety equipment or follow the rules of the activity. Look at Figure 7.4 to see some of the potential injuries that can be sustained through taking part in sport.

You would obviously be very unlucky to suffer all of these injuries, but even so you should try to minimise the risk of receiving any injuries. We have already discussed the need to carry out a physical readiness questionnaire, PAR-Q, (see Chapter 4) before starting on a programe of physical activity, to reduce the risk of triggering health issues as a result of a known medical condition. There are also other ways to reduce the risk of injury and therefore contribute to your general wellbeing, these are identified below.

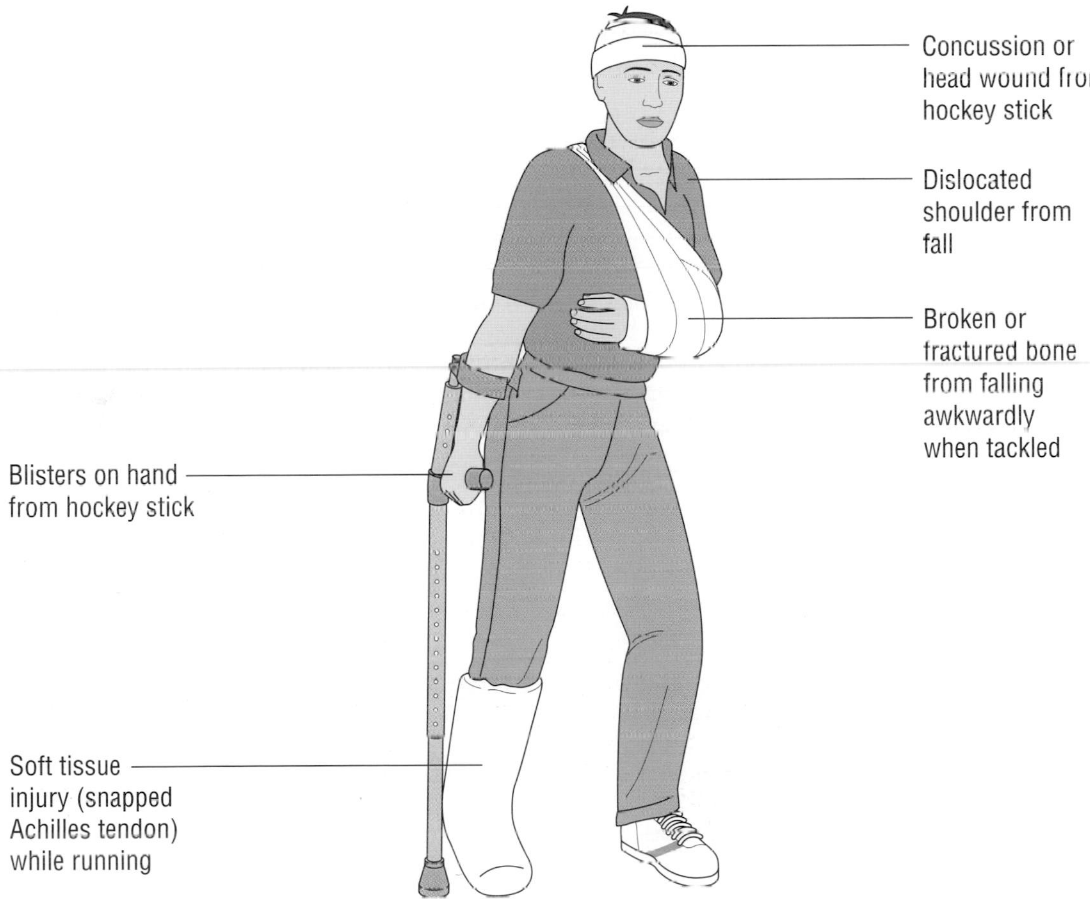

Figure 7.4 Possible sports injuries

WHY DO WE NEED RULES?

Rules are in place so that we can all enjoy playing sport. They make the sport fair and encourage good sporting behaviour; they also help to protect us from injury and maintain our safety.

E QUESTION

Look at Table 7.9. How might these rules protect the players?

RULE	WHAT INJURY MIGHT THIS PROTECT THE PLAYERS FROM?
No lifting the stick above head height	
Checking players' studs in their boots before they go onto the pitch	
Taping up or removal of any jewellery	

Table 7.9 Rules to protect players

ACTION 7

Choose one of the sports for which you will be assessed in your practical. Complete your own table, identifying three rules and how the rule protects the people playing. (Use different examples from those in Table 7.9.)

CLOTHING AND EQUIPMENT

Rules are not the only way of protecting yourself and others from injury. You need to use the correct

- kit
- protective clothing
- equipment and
- facilities.

Kit

Using the correct kit means that your movements will not be restricted by heavy or tight clothing or by clothing that is too baggy or loose (could you play rugby, football or hockey as well with your ordinary clothes on, compared with when you wear your sports kit?). Because your movements are not restricted your level of play should be higher, but you are also less likely to be injured if wearing the correct kit because your footwear will be appropriate for the surface you are playing on (grass, artificial pitch, track, tarmac, gym floor, sports hall; notice how your footwear tends to change as you change the surface you are playing on).

Also, loose clothing could be a problem in sports such as trampolining where it might catch; on the other hand, if clothing is too heavy or tight, you might not be able to perform the correct technique and become injured as a result.

E QUESTION

1. Why would wearing the correct kit reduce the risk of injury in trampolining?
2. Can you think of any protective clothing that you can wear when trampolining?
3. What items of safety equipment are used, or what checks to the equipment should be carried out to reduce risk of injury during a trampolining session?
4. How could the facilities lead to injury when trampolining?

Protective clothing

This is vital in some sports. For example, although the idea in hockey is to stop the ball with your stick, it will hit your shin from time to time. Depending on how hard the ball has been hit, this can be very painful unless you are wearing shin guards. Similarly, players wear mouth guards so that they do not lose their teeth if they are hit with a hockey stick or ball.

ACTION 8

Name the items of protective clothing in Figure 7.5, the correct sporting activity, and explain how they reduce risk of injury.

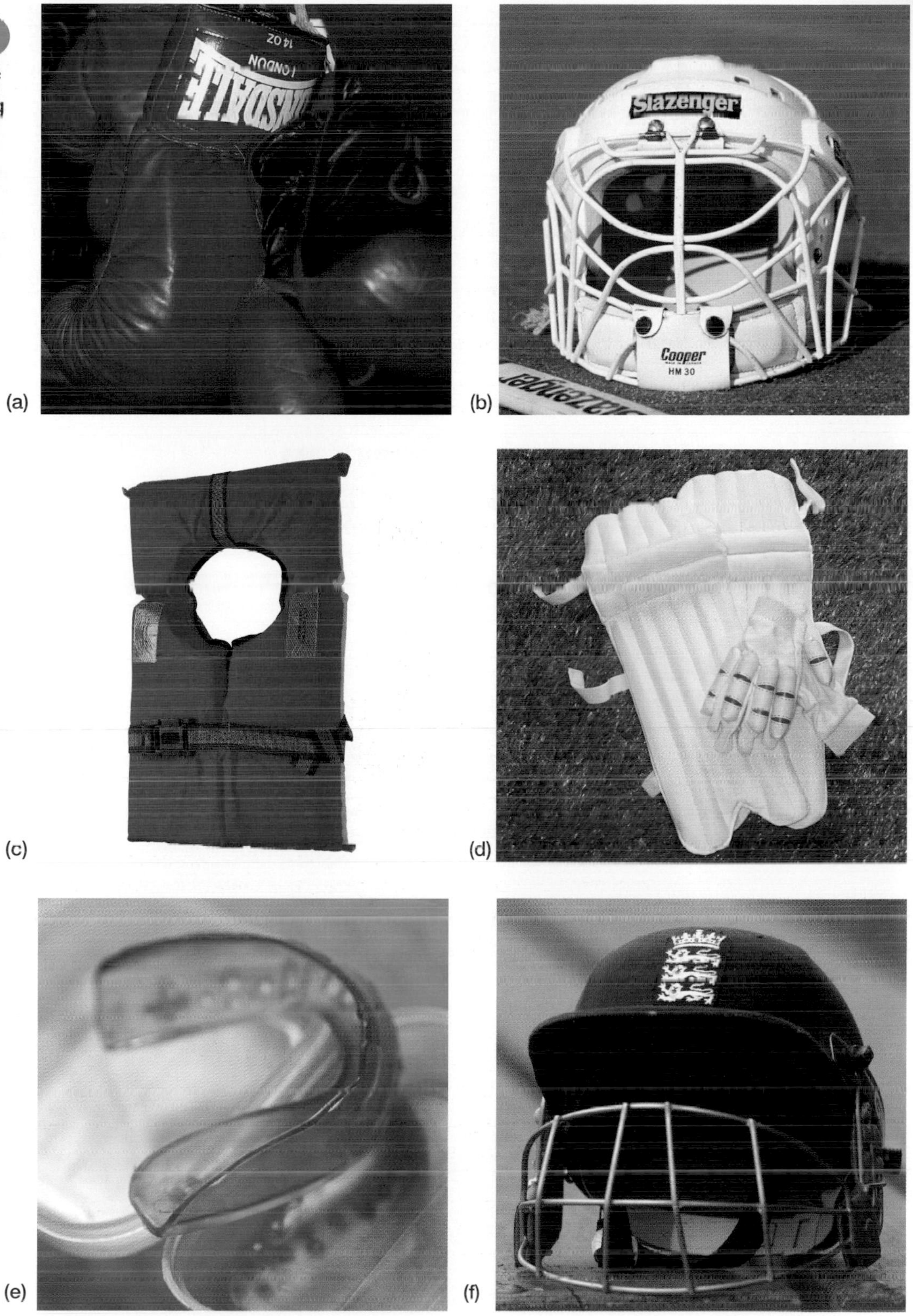

Figure 7.5 Protective clothing

ACTION 9

Look at the pictures in Figure 7.6. List the items of protective clothing, what they are being used to protect and the injury which they are designed to prevent.

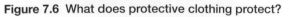

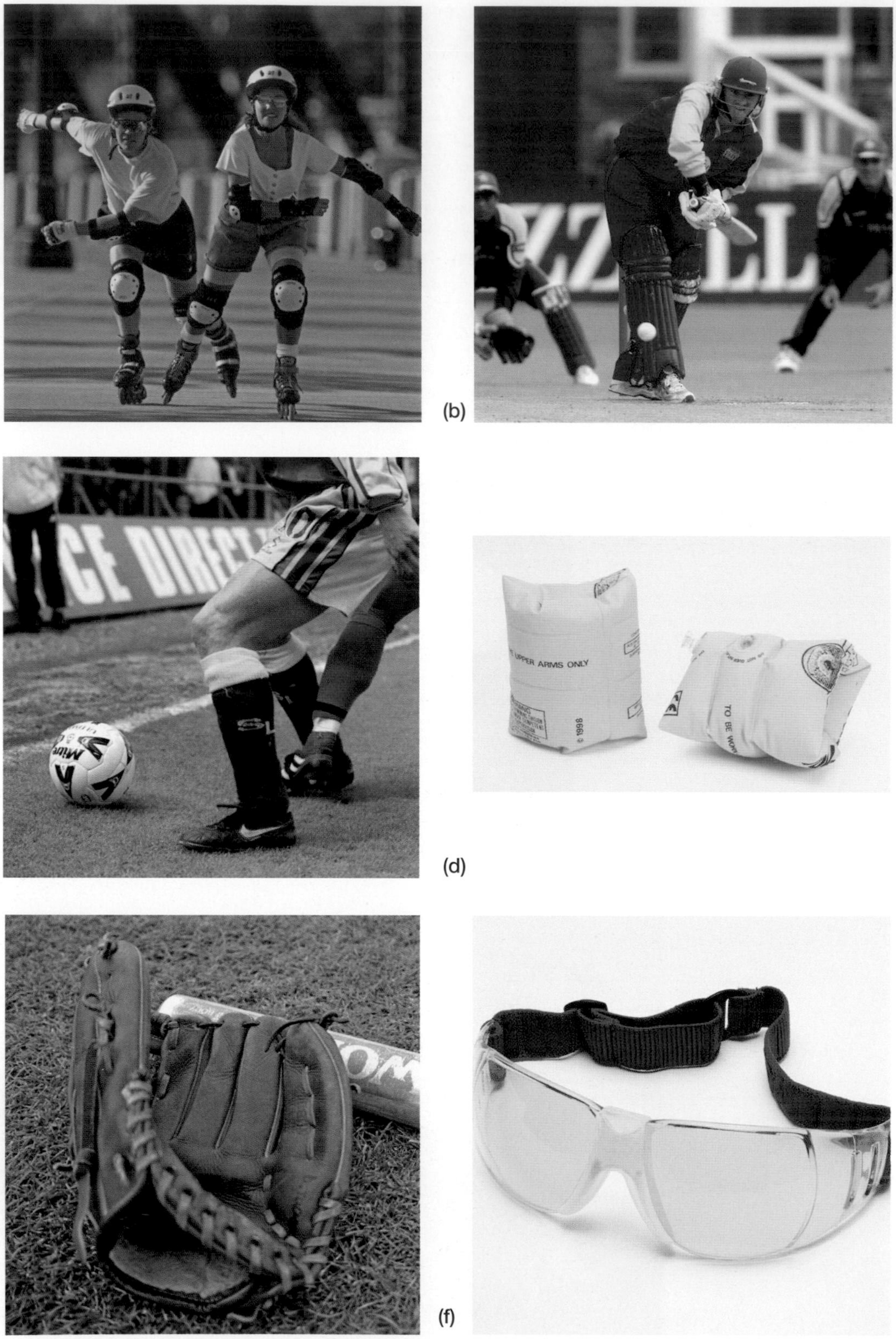

(a) (b) (c) (d) (e) (f)

Figure 7.6 What does protective clothing protect?

Figure 7.7 Padding around rugby posts

Equipment

You should always check the equipment you are going to use. Ask yourself, is it safe for use? If the answer is no, do not use it. For example:

- Playing squash or badminton with an inappropriate grip on the handle could lead to the racket flying out of your hand. This might not result in an injury to you, but could mean that a partner or opponent is hit with the racket.
- In basketball, if the hoop is damaged the court should not be used until it is fixed otherwise it could fall and injure those underneath it.
- In netball the goal posts should be checked to make sure the bolts securing the hoops are tight.

The equipment you use may also need some protective clothing! For example:

- Rugby posts have padding around them so that if players run into the posts in the heat of the game, the risk of injury is reduced.

Facilities

The correct facilities also need to be used for the sport that you are playing. Sports halls can be used for a variety of activities such as badminton, five-a-side football, netball, volleyball and table tennis, but if there is water on the floor making it slippery, the risk of injury is increased. Activities such as sprinting, however, should not be carried out in a sports hall unless the sprint stops well short of the end wall, or appropriate padding is placed at the end of the wall. Failure to do this would increase the risk of injury as sprinters could hit the end wall at pace, which would probably result in a broken bone. If rugby were played indoors, the rules about tackling would need to change, otherwise the risk of injury when players hit the hard floor would be too great. Other points to consider about facilities include:

- trampolining should only be carried out if the height of the facility allows it
- rugby matches are cancelled if the pitch is frozen
- outdoor netball matches are cancelled if the court is too icy
- long jump pits should always be checked for 'unwanted objects' before use.

Figure 7.8 Long jump pits should be checked before use

ACTION 10

Work with a partner and think about what issues you should consider regarding facilities for the following activities:
- basketball
- swimming
- discus
- boxing.

Balancing competition

This aspect of sport is also used to help reduce the risk of injury. This means that the competition rules try to make sure that the competition is fair by having evenly matched opposition. This is achieved by making sure that people only compete directly with each other if they are:

- a similar age, or
- the same sex, or
- a similar ability, or
- a similar weight.

E QUESTION

How is competition balanced in other activities, e.g. boxing and badminton?

For example, football competitions will be for different age groups, U12, U13, U14. The U12 side would not play the U21 side. The competition would not be fair because of the size of the U21s compared with the U12s, and their level of skill and experience. Apart from being a poor game because of the inequalities, it would increase the risk of injury to the U12 side. For the same reason, men's and women's football teams do not normally play against each other. The same is true in other sports.

Warm up and cool down

A proper warm up before activity should also reduce the chance of risk of soft tissue injury and a thorough cool down will reduce the chance of muscle soreness after the activity. See Chapter 5 for more detail on warm up and cool down.

JUDGING RISKS IN SPORTING ACTIVITY

When calculating risk in relation to different activities, think about the environment – is it naturally dangerous? For example, mountains, fast-flowing rivers, and the sea will all provide greater risks than activities conducted in less dangerous environments such as sports halls.

The next activities ask you to judge the risks of various activities. When asked to complete this sort of activity, you should consider the following questions before arriving at a conclusion:

- What would happen if the risk were not prevented? How bad would it be?

Therefore, if offered the choice between archery and badminton, you might decide that archery had the greatest risk as potentially you could do more damage in this activity than badminton. This would be a reasonable conclusion.

- What is the ability/experience of the group taking part in the activity?

If you had a group of beginners white-water rafting, would there be any greater risk than if they were all experienced? You might decide that the inexperienced or beginners group would be at greater risk as they were more likely to get into difficulty, and if they did they would not know how to escape it. Again, this would be a reasonable conclusion. When you cannot tell whether the people are beginners or not, just consider the first question to help you make your judgement.

Figure 7.9 What are the risks?

ACTION 11

Look at the pictures in Figure 7.9. Identify some of the risks and the possible precautions against those risks for each sporting activity. Enter your answers in Table 7.10 and discuss them with others in your group.

SPORT	RISK (WHAT COULD HAPPEN TO YOU?)	PRECAUTION (HOW COULD YOU HELP TO PREVENT THE RISK HAPPENING?)
Netball		
White-water rafting		
1500 metres		
Rugby		
Gymnastics		
Climbing		

Table 7.10 Risks and precautions

QUESTION

Which of the activities pictured in Figure 7.9 presents the greatest risk? Justify your answer.

CHAPTER 8 A HEALTHY, ACTIVE LIFESTYLE AND YOUR CARDIOVASCULAR SYSTEM

GOALS

By the end of this chapter you should be able to:

- **define heart rate, stroke volume, cardiac output, blood pressure and cholesterol and the effects of exercise on them**
- **describe the immediate and short-term effects of physical activity on the cardiovascular system**
- **describe the effects of regular exercise and the long-term benefits of physical activity on the cardiovascular system**
- **explain the effects of diet on cholesterol levels and blood pressure**
- **explain the effects of recreational drugs (alcohol, nicotine) on blood pressure.**

The following four chapters of the book look at the systems within the human body. The reason you need to know about these systems is that they all have a big impact on our ability to take part in sport and on the level of performance we can achieve. Not all of the content included in these chapters is required for your examination. This content is signposted – look out for the NE (not examined) although it might help with Science revision! The reason for including this content is to give some background to the body systems. Without this knowledge, some of the things you need to know and will be tested on will be more difficult to understand, and besides, it's interesting!

This chapter looks at the cardiovascular system – the heart, blood and blood vessels. The cardiovascular system is vital for sporting performance as it is responsible for:

- transporting increased levels of oxygen (needed to release energy to perform and/or recover from performance) around the body to where it is needed
- regulating our temperature so that we do not overheat during exercise
- removing waste such as carbon dioxide and lactic acid.

Although this chapter looks at the cardiovascular system, there are clear links with the respiratory system, as this is how we receive the air containing oxygen into our bodies. The two systems together are known as the cardio-respiratory system.

THE HEART NE

The heart works continuously throughout our lives. In an average lifetime it can beat over three billion times (try working it out: average heart rate (72 bpm) × number of minutes in a day × number of days in a year × average life expectancy (80). This is a resting value for the heart rate; if we exercise, it beats even more.

ACTION 1

These are all key components of the heart:

- atria, ventricles, septum, tricuspid valve, bicuspid valve, semi-lunar valves, aorta, vena cava, pulmonary artery, pulmonary vein.

Using the description in the text below label Figure 8.1.

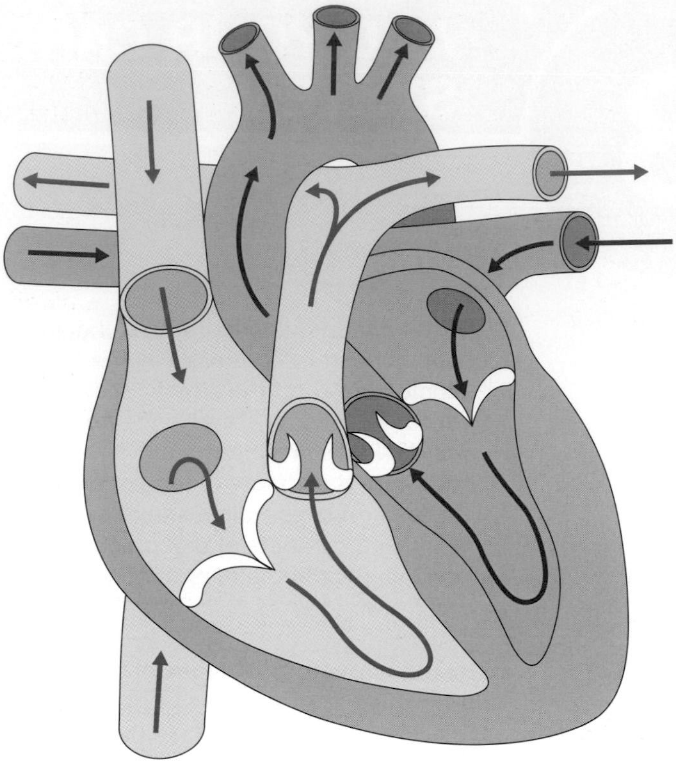

Figure 8.1 The heart

The heart is made up of four chambers. The top two chambers are called atria and the bottom chambers are the ventricles. They are assigned a side, left or right. This is the first tricky bit. When labelling the heart you have to imagine that it is in your body when deciding which is left and right. Which is the right side of your body? If you were to look at a photograph of the side you have just identified, your right would appear to be your left! If you pick up the photograph and turn it to face the same way that you are facing, your right side is back where it belongs, on the right of your body. The same is true with the heart, so when you look at a diagram, do not forget to imagine it inside your body.

The left and right atria receive blood into the heart and pass it onto the ventricles when they contract.

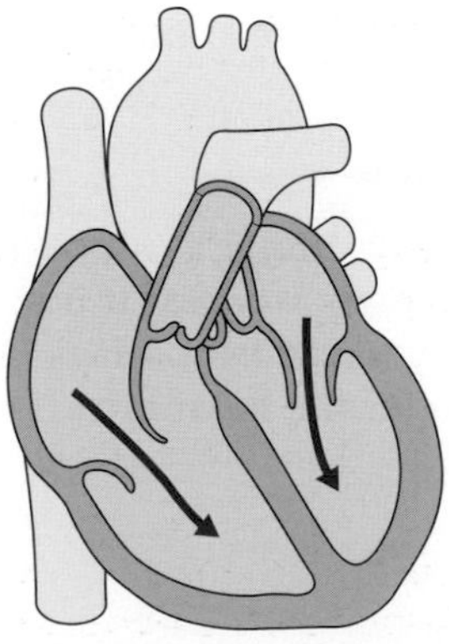

Figure 8.2 Ventricles fill with blood due to the contraction of the atria

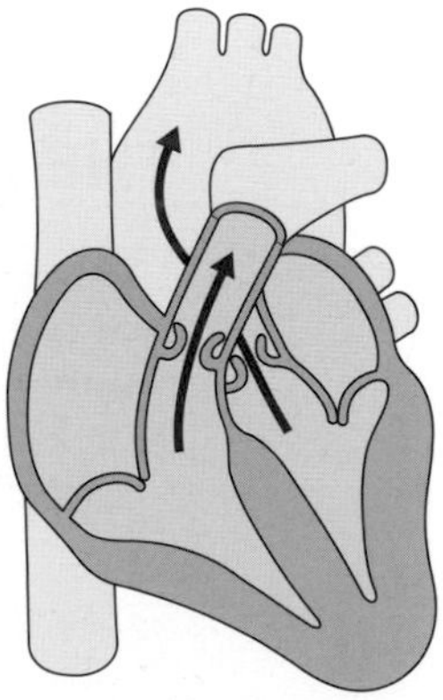

Figure 8.3 Ventricles contract to force blood out

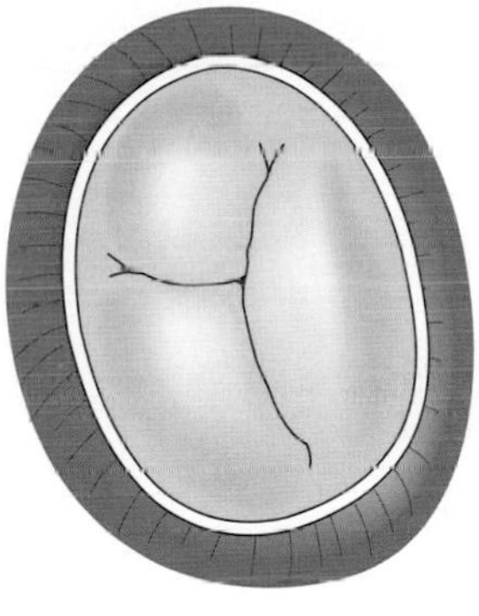

Figure 8.4 The valve controls the direction of the blood flow. When closed no blood can flow through

QUESTION

Can you think why it is important that blood is not allowed to go back the way it has just come? What would happen when the ventricles contract if there were no valves between the ventricles and the atria?

The left atrium receives oxygenated blood from the lungs through the pulmonary vein, and the right atrium receives de-oxygenated blood from the body through the vena cava (this is also a vein). Notice that atria is the plural form of atrium, i.e. you use it when talking about both atria rather than just one atrium.

Oxygenated means that the blood has picked up oxygen from the lungs (more on that in the next chapter). De-oxygenated means that the oxygen that was being carried by the blood has been removed or taken by the body's tissues to use in order to release energy.

The left and right ventricles receive blood from the atria above them; once they have received the blood they contract to force the blood out of the heart.

- The left ventricle has a thicker muscular wall because it has to do the most work. It is from here that blood is pumped out of the heart via the aorta to the rest of the body. The aorta is an artery.
- The right ventricle only pumps blood as far as the lungs, via the pulmonary artery to pick up more oxygen.

Two sets of valves are found in the heart. Valves are flaps which only allow blood to flow one way, like emergency exit doors that hinge one way to let you out, but close after you so that you cannot go back the way you came.

If blood were allowed to flow backwards, it might not be pushed to the lungs to collect extra oxygen or be pumped around the body to the tissues that need to receive oxygenated blood. In other words, we would be unlikely to receive the oxygen we need to exercise.

The tricuspid valve is on the right side of the heart (one way to remember this is to think of a saying e.g. 'its all right to watch TV': TV stands for tricuspid valve, and it is on the right). It separates the right atrium from the right ventricle, allowing blood to flow from the atrium to the ventricle.

The bicuspid valve is on the left side of the heart separating the left atrium from the left ventricle. It allows blood to flow from the left atrium to the left ventricle but not the other way.

The remaining valves between the left ventricle and the aorta, and the right ventricle and the pulmonary artery, are called the semi-lunar valves. These valves allow the movement of blood from the ventricles out of the heart, but once it has left, the blood is not allowed to return.

The septum is the wall between the two sides of the heart, dividing left and right. This wall is required because the right side of the heart contains blood from the body which has been de-oxygenated, whereas the blood on the left side of the heart contains oxygenated blood. If the blood were allowed to mix, the performer would receive a drop in the amount of oxygen being delivered to the muscles, so they would be unable to release as much energy for physical work.

You should now be able to finish labelling your diagram. Compare your answers with those shown in Figure 8.5.

QUESTION

If blood is oxygenated once it leaves the lungs, what has happened in the lungs? If blood returning to the heart from the body is de-oxygenated, what has happened to the oxygen?

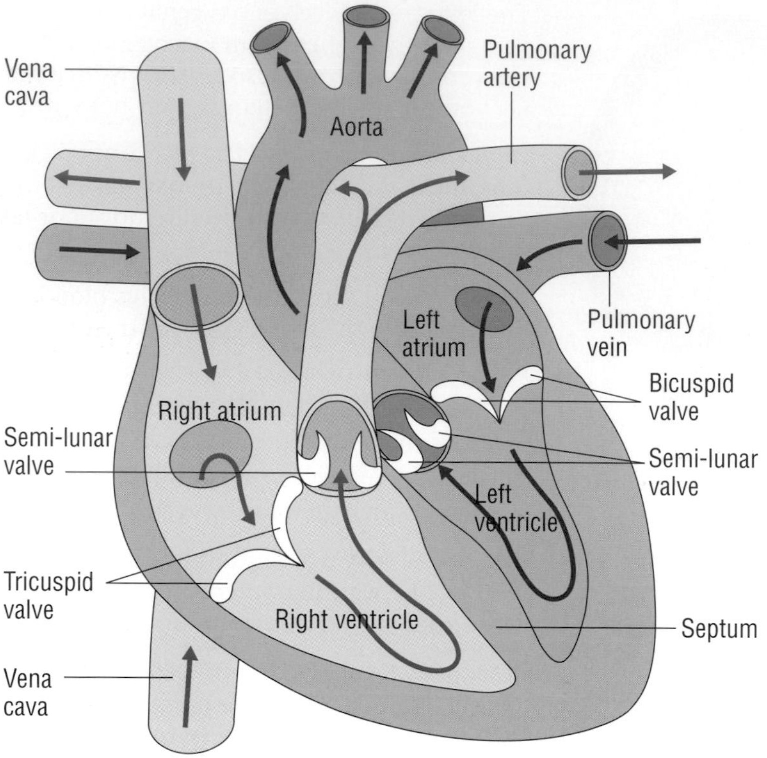

Figure 8.5 Labelled diagram of the heart

Double circulatory system NE

As the heart pumps, it circulates blood. Blood is circulated from the heart to the lungs and then back to the heart (circuit 1, the pulmonary circulation). Blood is also circulated from the heart to the rest of the body and back again (circuit 2, the systemic circulation). Because of these two clear areas that are circulated (lungs and the rest of the body), it is known as a double circulatory system.

ACTION 2

Starting with blood entering the heart from the body, take it in turns to state the next stage of circulation. You should say whether blood is entering or leaving and which vessel or chamber it enters or leaves through, as well as the valves involved, until you have completed the route of the blood in the double circulation.

Blood vessels NE

Blood vessels carry blood to all the living cells in the body. There are different types of blood vessels: arteries, arterioles, capillaries, venules and veins. Each type of blood vessel has a specific job to do, and is structured differently so that it can do its job effectively.

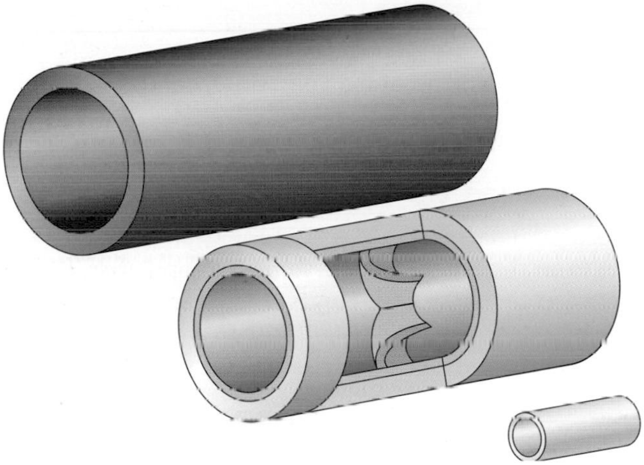

Figure 8.6 Arteries, capillaries and veins

E QUESTION

Can you work out which of the blood vessels in Figure 8.6 is which, from the information given about arteries, capillaries and veins?

Arteries NE

These carry blood away from the heart, which is easy to remember as away and arteries both start with the letter A. The aorta, the main artery, also starts with an A.

Arteries are made up of three layers. The outside layer is tough, the middle layer is muscular and the inner layer is smooth to make it easy for the blood to pass through.

Things to know about arteries:

- They carry blood away from the heart.
- They carry blood at higher pressure than the other vessels because they take blood from the heart.
- They have thick muscular walls.
- They pulsate: when the heart relaxes, the artery muscle contracts, pushing the blood forward.
- Because they carry blood away from the heart they carry oxygenated blood (there is ONE exception to this, see the Question box).

E QUESTION

What is the name of the artery which carries de-oxygenated blood away from the heart?

Veins NE

Veins carry blood back to the heart. The main vein is called the vena cava.

Things to know about veins:

- They carry blood towards the heart.
- They carry blood at low pressure.
- They have valves.
- They have thin walls.
- They have a larger internal lumen (the space in the middle of the vessel) than arteries.
- Because they carry blood back to the heart, they carry de-oxygenated blood (there is ONE exception to this).

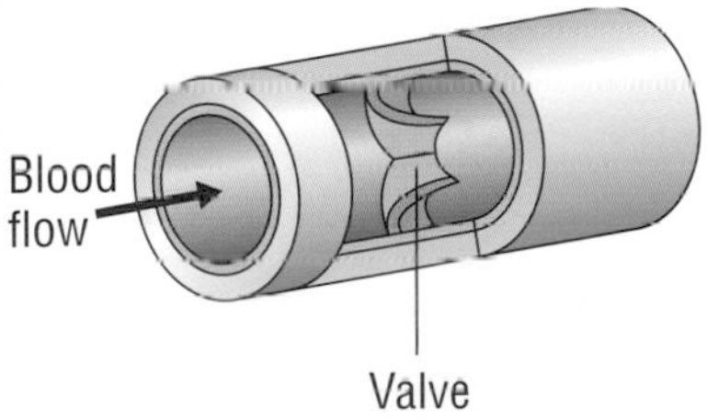

Figure 8.7 A vein showing a valve

E QUESTION

What is the name of the vein which carries oxygenated blood to the heart?

Capillaries NE

If arteries take blood away from the heart and veins bring it back, how does the blood get from the artery into the vein? Via capillaries, the vessels which form the link between the other two. This is where carbon dioxide will diffuse from the tissues into the blood, and oxygen will diffuse from the blood to the tissues. See Figure 8.8 – the fine network of blood vessels between the larger two are the capillaries.

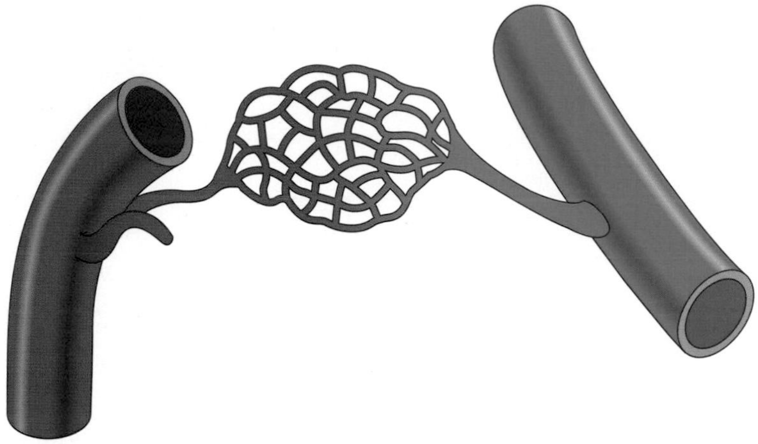

Figure 8.8 Capillaries between the larger blood vessels

Things to remember about capillaries:

- They are the link between arterioles (which then link to arteries) and venules (which then link to veins).
- They are one cell thick and very fragile.
- Blood cells pass through them one cell at a time (giving time for the exchange of gases to take place).

ACTION 3

Use the descriptions of the blood vessels in this chapter to help you decide whether the following descriptions are of arteries, capillaries or veins:

1. I always travel away from the heart.
2. I am the link between the other two types of blood vessels.
3. I have thin walls.
4. I normally carry oxygenated blood.
5. I have thick muscular walls.
6. I have a small lumen (the lumen is the space in the middle of the vessel).
7. I allow the exchange of gases and nutrients with the cells of the body.
8. I always travel towards the heart.
9. I pulsate.
10. I work under high pressure.

THE BLOOD

Blood is made up of red blood cells, white blood cells, platelets and plasma. Adults have around 5.5 litres of blood circulating their bodies. Plasma is the liquid part of the blood, mainly made up of water. If the plasma did not exist, the solid cells would not be able to flow around the body, so the plasma gives the other cells a ride.

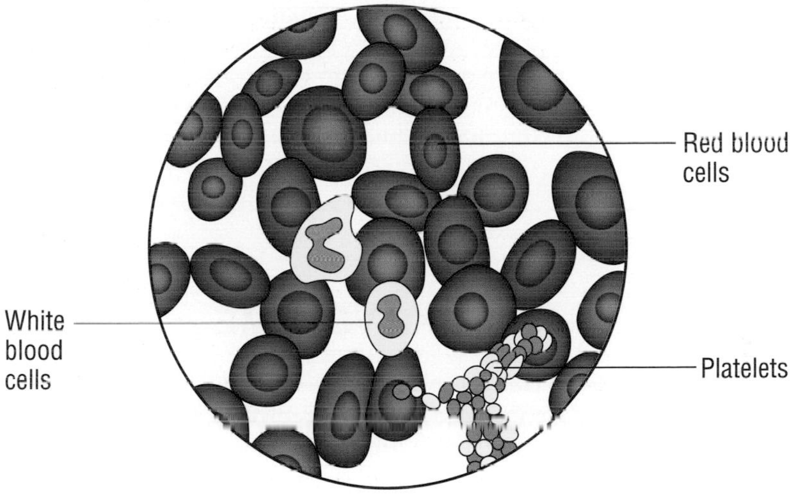

Figure 8.9 Blood cells

Red blood cells

These are very important to a performer. The red blood cells contain haemoglobin, a substance which allows the transportation of oxygen around the body. In blood doping and the use of EPO, mentioned in Chapter 7, the performer increases the number of red blood cells they have in their blood, so that they can carry more oxygen to aid their performance, despite the risk of unhealthy side effects.

White blood cells

These are also very important to the performer. They are responsible for seeking out and destroying infections. The white cells can slide through the walls of the blood vessel and attack bacteria at the site of the infection. The white blood cells help keep the athlete healthy.

Platelets

These play a vital role in maintaining the health of a sports performer. Platelets aid clotting: if the performer receives a cut or a graze, platelets are dispatched to put a plug in the hole in the skin so that there is no further blood loss.

HEART RATE

Heart rate
The number of times the heart beats per minute.

Heart rate refers to the number of times the heart beats per minute. Each time the heart beats the ventricles contract, squeezing blood out of the heart into the lungs or the rest of the body. During exercise we need to increase the rate of blood flow, in other words, we need to make the blood flow faster so that we can deliver oxygen more quickly to the working muscles and remove waste products such as carbon dioxide at a quicker rate.This means that the performer can keep working at a higher level of intensity than when they are at rest. This increase in blood flow is mainly achieved through increasing the heart rate.

ACTION 4

Working in pairs, measure each other's resting heart rate and make a note of it. Find your pulse and then count the number of times you feel the blood pulsate under your fingers in a minute.) You need to stay calm and quiet while your pulse is being measured as any movement or sudden noise will make your heart beat faster.

Take it in turns to carry out some exercise. This could be jumping up and down, or running on the spot for two minutes. Immediately after your exercise, ask your partner to measure your heart rate again and make a note of it. Then swap roles.

There should be a difference in your heart rate after exercise. Was it higher or lower? Why has your heart rate changed in this way?

Stroke volume
The amount of blood ejected from the heart per beat.

Be careful not to confuse stroke volume and cardiac output. Try to think of stroke volume as a single stroke/beat of the heart. Cardiac output relates to the total output from the heart in one minute

Cardiac output
The amount of blood leaving the heart per minute

ACTION 5

What would the cardiac output be for a performer at rest with a heart rate of 70bpm and stroke volume of 70ml?

STROKE VOLUME

This is the amount of blood ejected from the heart per beat. When the ventricles contract, they do not empty completely of blood; only about 60 per cent of the blood is ejected. With exercise, the muscles of the wall of the heart surrounding the ventricles become stronger so that when they contract they can do so more forcibly. When this happens, they can squeeze harder on the blood in the ventricles and therefore push more out of the heart. This is why stroke volume increases with regular exercise. Think of a balloon filled with water: if you squeeze it a little, a small amount of water comes out, but if you squeeze it harder, more water will be ejected.

The increase in stroke volume that is achieved through training also explains why fit performers tend to have lower resting heart rates than those who do not train.

CARDIAC OUTPUT

This is the amount of blood ejected from the heart per minute. It is calculated by multiplying heart rate (the number of times the heart beats per minute) by stroke volume (the amount of blood that is ejected from the heart per beat).

cardiac output = heart rate × stroke volume

At rest we need in the region of five litres of blood to circulate our bodies, but this figure can rise dramatically during exercise to 30 litres of blood per minute. Link this to Chapter 6 in relation to redistribution of blood flow and you can see that the active muscles could receive as much as 25 litres of blood per minute during intense exercise.

E QUESTION

Looking at the equation below for cardiac output – can you work out why fit performers have lower resting heart rates than those who do not train?

Cardiac output = Heart Rate × Stroke Volume

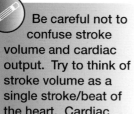

E QUESTION

Look at the two images of Kelly Holmes: in Figure 8.10 she is resting after completing her race, and in Figure 8.11 she is in the middle of her event. While she is running she will need to deliver more oxygen to her muscles than when she is at rest. She will also need to remove the increased carbon dioxide that is being created during exercise, therefore she needs to increase her cardiac output. Remember, cardiac output = stroke volume × heart rate. What, therefore, are the two ways she can increase her cardiac output?

Figure 8.10 Kelly Holmes at rest

Figure 8.11 Kelly Holmes in action

BLOOD PRESSURE

E QUESTION

Which type of blood vessel contains arterial blood?

As the blood moves through the blood vessels it exerts a force on the the sides of the blood vessel it is travelling through. The strength of this force is your blood pressure. As the blood circulates further from the heart the force it exerts reduces, so blood pressure decreases as the blood moves through the arteries, arterioles, capillaries, venules and veins. When blood pressure is measured (as part of a health check) arterial blood pressure is used.

Blood pressure is checked because if your blood pressure is too high, it puts extra strain on your arteries (and your heart) which may lead to heart attacks and strokes.

In the section on the heart there was a description of how the ventricles in the heart relax to allow them to fill with blood and then contract to expel the blood around the body. When the ventricles contract blood pressure is at its greatest, this is called systolic blood pressure. When the ventricles are filling, the blood pressure is lower (you would expect this as blood is not being forced out of the heart), this is the diastolic blood pressure.

When your blood pressure is measured it will be written as two numbers. For example, if your reading is 120/80mmHg, your blood pressure is 120 over 80.

Most people can control their blood pressure by following an active and healthy lifestyle. The Blood Pressure Association recommends five steps to a healthy blood pressure:

- eat less salt in your diet
- eat more fruit and vegetables
- keep to a healthy weight
- drink less alcohol
- exercise.

CHOLESTEROL

Cholesterol is made in the liver from the fatty foods that we eat. It is needed in small quantities for essential processes within the body, (it forms part of some hormones and insulates nerve fibers). There are two main types of cholesterol:

- Low density lipoprotein (LDL).
- High density lipoprotein (HDL).

HDL transports cholesterol away from the cells back to the liver to be broken down, therefore this is considered to be 'good' cholesterol.

LDL however is the 'bad' cholesterol. It can increase arterial disease due to a narrowing of the artery caused by a build up of the cholesterol. This increases the risk of heart attack and stroke.

The amount of cholesterol present in the blood can range from 3.6 to 7.8mmol/litre (A mmol/l is a standard measurement for describing the concentration of something. In this case cholesterol. It stands for millimoles/litre.). More than 6mmol/litre is considered high. Current Government advice recommends a target cholesterol level of less than 5mmol/litre.

Cholesterol levels can be reduced by:

- eating a diet that is low in saturated fats
- taking regular exercise.

IMMEDIATE EFFECTS OF EXERCISE ON THE CARDIOVASCULAR SYSTEM

As soon as you take part in physical activity your body experiences some immediate effects. These are changes that take place straight away to give immediate help, so that you can complete the work you are asking of your body. Once exercise has stopped your body will slowly return back to its pre-exercise state. The immediate changes to the cardiovascular system are:

- heart rate increases to speed up oxygen delivery to the muscles
- during aerobic exercise systolic blood pressure rises progressively, while diastolic blood pressure stays the same or decreases slightly
- blood pressure increases (due to increased blood flow as a result of higher heart rate).

E QUESTION

What is aerobic exercise?

E QUESTION

What is the difference between systolic and diastolic blood pressure?

E QUESTION

What are the principles of training?

E QUESTION

How would vasodilation of the blood vessel help to reduce blood pressure?

EFFECTS OF REGULAR TRAINING ON THE CARDIOVASCULAR SYSTEM

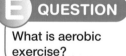

If you continue to exercise on a regular basis, following the principles of training, your body will start to adapt to its increased workload, so that in effect the work becomes easier for the body to do (in other words, you become fitter). These adaptations are what you should refer to if asked about the effects of regular training on the cardiovascular system:

- increased strength of heart muscle
- increased size of heart
- increased stroke volume (due to increased strength of cardiac muscle)
- increased maximum cardiac output
- increased capillarisation
- increase in number of red blood cells
- drop in resting heart rate (due to increased stroke volume)
- quicker recovery rate after exercise
- healthier veins and arteries. Activity reduces the chance of fluid building up in the legs due to sedentary lifestyles.

LONG-TERM HEALTH BENEFITS OF EXERCISE ON THE CARDIOVASCULAR SYSTEM

ACTION 6

Explain to your partner why an increase in stroke volume will lead to a drop in resting heart rate.

Changes to the body as a result of regular exercise can also bring about long-term benefits. The long term benefits of exercise on the cardiovascular system are:

- drop in blood pressure
- reduction in cholesterol levels
- reduction in likelihood of coronary heart failure
- reduction in likelihood of a stroke.

When asked a question on this aspect of the course, make sure you double-check whether you are being asked about:

- the immediate effects of exercise
- the effects of regular training, or
- the long-term benefits of exercise.

Obviously these three areas are linked. We experience the immediate effects of exercise, which on a regular basis (through regular exercise) become permanent adaptations (while the level of activity is maintained). These adaptations then bring health benefits.

THE EFFECTS OF SMOKING AND ALCOHOL ON CARDIOVASCULAR HEALTH

Smoking

The banning of smoking in public places was brought about due to growing evidence that passive smoking as well as active smoking is harmful to our health, leading to heart and lung disease, cancer and premature death.

- If you smoke, you are two to three times more likely to have a heart attack than a non-smoker, and much more likely to die from heart disease. Smokers are also more likely to have strokes, blood clots, and angina.

ACTION 7

Complete the crossword on the cardiovascular system.

Alcohol

The general effects of alcohol are discussed in Chapter 7.

Long-term effects of drinking too much alcohol in relation to the cardiovascular system include heart failure and high blood pressure.

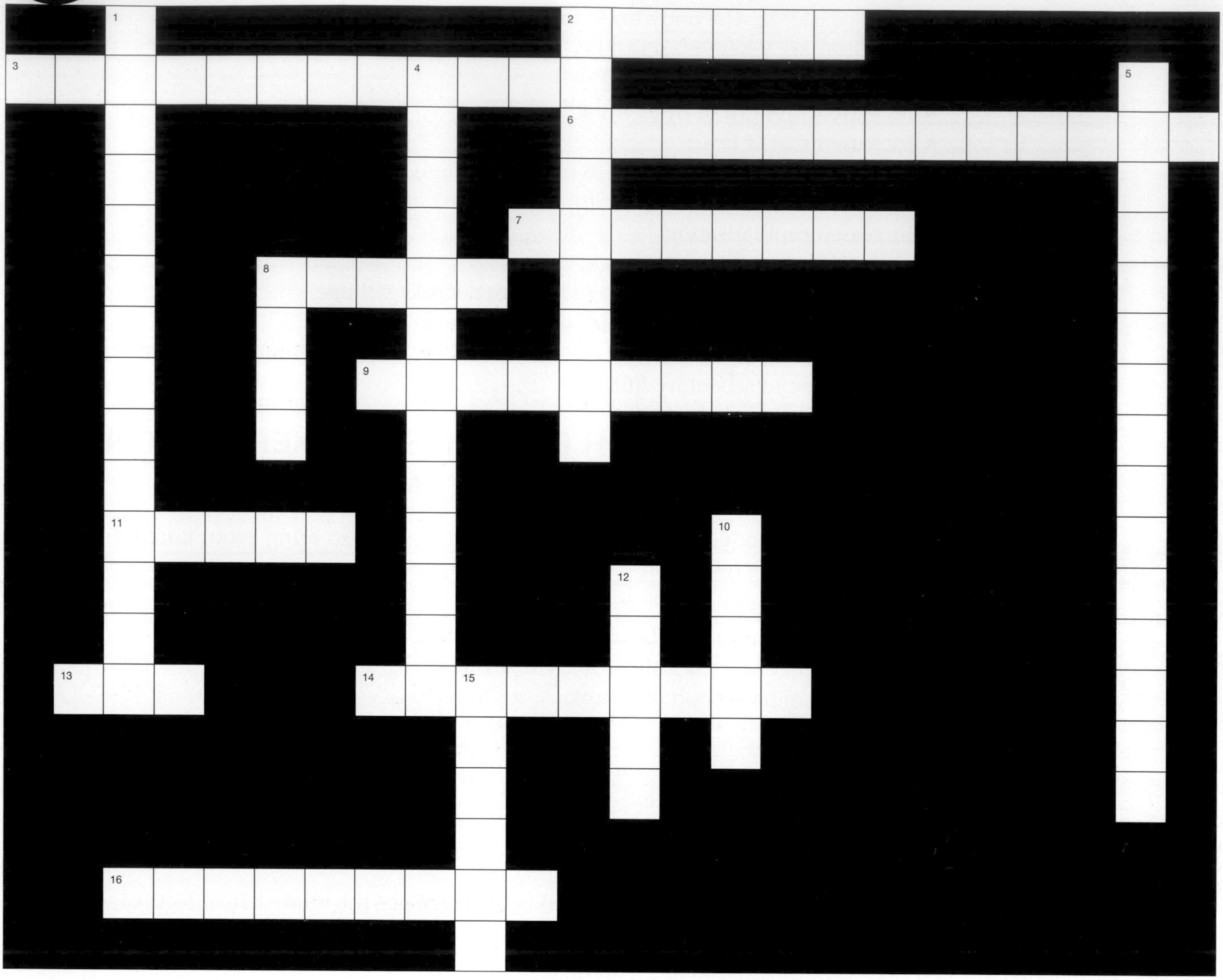

Across:

2 What type of circulatory systems do humans have? (6)

3 What is being defined? 'The amount of blood leaving the heart per beat' (6,6)

6 If I increase stroke volume, what else will increase? (7, 6)

7 Main vein in the body, brings blood back to the heart (4, 4)

8 What is the name of the structure that stops blood flowing the wrong way? (5)

9 What happens to the heart rate during exercise? (9)

11 The chambers in the top half of the heart (5)

13 Which blood cells carry oxygen to help the performer work for longer? (3)

14 Which term is represented in this equation as a question mark? Cardiac output × ? = SV (5,4)

16 Which blood vessel has this characteristic? Only allows blood to pass through one cell at a time (9)

Down:

1 Found on the right side of the heart, it prevents the back flow of blood (9,5)

2 What happens to the resting heart rate as a result of regular training? (9)

4 The strongest of the muscular walls around the chambers of the heart (4,9)

5 Takes deoxygenated blood away from the heart. (9,6)

8 Which blood vessel has very thin walls? (4)

10 Which blood cells protect the performer from infection? (5)

12 Takes oxygenated blood away from the heart (5)

15 Which blood vessel has a thick muscular wall? (6)

CHAPTER 9 A HEALTHY, ACTIVE LIFESTYLE AND YOUR RESPIRATORY SYSTEM

GOALS

By the end of this chapter you should be able to:

- describe the biomechanical aspects of respiration
- explain the difference between aerobic and anaerobic respiration and link to lactic acid production and oxygen debt
- describe the immediate and short-term effects of physical activity on the respiratory system
- describe the effects of regular exercise and the long-term benefits of physical activity on the respiratory system
- explain the effects of recreational drugs (alcohol, nicotine) on alveoli-gaseous exchange.

In the previous chapter we looked at the importance of the cardiovascular system in transporting blood carrying oxygen to our working muscles and the rest of the body. The respiratory system is also vital to the performer, because without it the performer would not be able to receive air (containing oxygen) into the body for the cardiovascular system to circulate, nor would it be able to expel carbon dioxide from the body. These are the main functions of the lungs.

http://www.brianmac.co.uk/physiolr.htm
Gives a summary of the respiratory system to reinforce aspects of the text.

COMPOSITION OF INSPIRED AND EXPIRED AIR NE

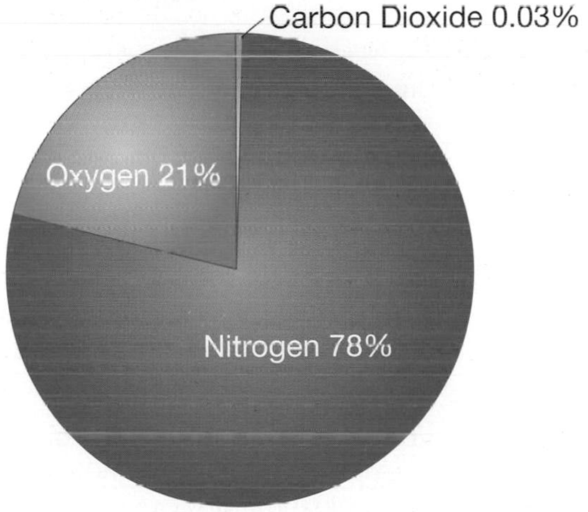

Figure 9.1 Shows the relative percentages of gases in the air we breathe in

As you can see from Figure 9.1, the air we breathe in is approximately 78 per cent nitrogen, 21 per cent oxygen, and 0.03 per cent carbon dioxide. Traces of water vapour are also present but the figure will vary depending on the weather. (Not surprisingly, if it is raining there is more water vapour in the air.) For your course you need to understand if any of these values change and, if they do, the reason why they change.

There are some traces of other gases in air as well, but these are in very small amounts (and not on your course). It is useful to know they exist as this explains why, when you add up the percentages of oxygen, carbon dioxide and nitrogen in air they do not equal 100 per cent. The missing points of a percentage are due to the traces of these other gases.

We all need oxygen to release energy, but when participating exercising we need more, because we need more energy. The efficiency of the respiratory system in getting oxygen into the body, and the cardiovascular system in delivering it where it is needed, will have a big impact on the level of performance achieved in most sporting activities. For example, imagine the 1500 metre runner who could only walk or do a slow jog because he could not breathe enough oxygen into his body to provide enough energy to go any faster.

Figure 9.2 Endurance athletes have very efficient respiratory systems so that oxygen can be used to release energy for longer

EXPIRATION AND INSPIRATION NE

Inspiration and expiration
Breathing in and breathing out

Air must travel through the respiratory system to arrive at the lungs, but what do we physically do to help us breathe in and out? The movement of the diaphragm and the ribs helps the movement of air into and out of the lungs.

During expiration (breathing out), the lungs slightly deflate (like a balloon losing some of the air inside it). When this happens the lungs do not take up as much room and so the ribs can move downwards and inwards and the diaphragm can relax (move up). This helps the lungs to expel some of the air inside them.

During inspiration (breathing in) however, the lungs need to expand so they can hold more air, like a balloon being inflated. In order to make room for the lungs to do this, the diaphragm contracts (this pulls it tight and flat, see Figure 9.5), and the ribs move up and out due to the contraction of the external intercostal muscles (these attach one rib to the rib below it – the muscle runs downwards from the upper rib and fowards to the rib below).

The number of times we inspire and expire in one minute is known as our ventilation rate. During exercise, the ventilation rate increases: an average adult male will inspire and expire between 10 to 14 times a minute at rest, but this can increase to 25 times a minute during heavy exercise. Try measuring your breathing rate by placing your hands across your chest (opposite hand to opposite shoulder) and counting the rise and fall of the rib cage. It is difficult to count accurately, but you should be able to feel a difference while at rest and immediately after exercise.

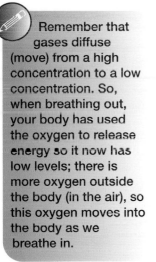

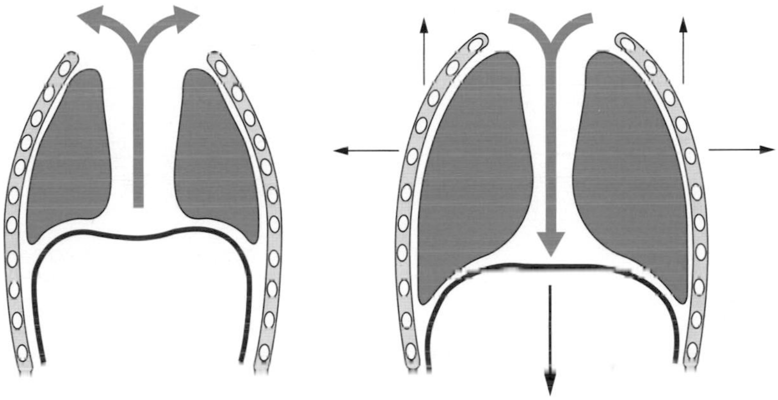

Figure 9.3 Movement of ribs and diaphragm during expiration and inspiration

QUESTION

Why does the inspiration and expiration rate increase in this way as a result of exercise?

ALVEOLI-GASEOUS EXCHANGE

The alveoli in the lungs are very important; it is here that the exchange of gases takes place. Gaseous exchange is the swapping of oxygen and carbon dioxide due to the pressure gradients of each of the gases at the site of the exchange. For example, the percentage of oxygen in the lungs is much higher than that in the blood vessels arriving at the lungs. Due to the pressure difference (gradient), the oxygen diffuses from the lungs to the blood. Meanwhile, the percentage of carbon dioxide in the blood is higher than that in the lungs, and so this gas diffuses from the blood to the lungs. The gases are therefore 'swapped'.

Regular endurance training will result in an increase in the number of alveoli present in the lungs.

Remember that gases diffuse (move) from a high concentration to a low concentration. So, when breathing out, your body has used the oxygen to release energy so it now has low levels; there is more oxygen outside the body (in the air), so this oxygen moves into the body as we breathe in.

QUESTION

Why do you think it is an advantage for endurance athletes or sports performers to have a greater number of alveoli?

An increase in alveoli means that the performer can diffuse more oxygen into the blood, provided that the alveoli have access to a blood supply for the exchange of gases (see Figure 9.4). This is why there is an increase in the number of capillaries available. These two factors combined will lead to greater oxygen uptake during exercise, and therefore potentially more oxygen available to release energy, helping to fuel exercise for longer.

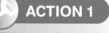

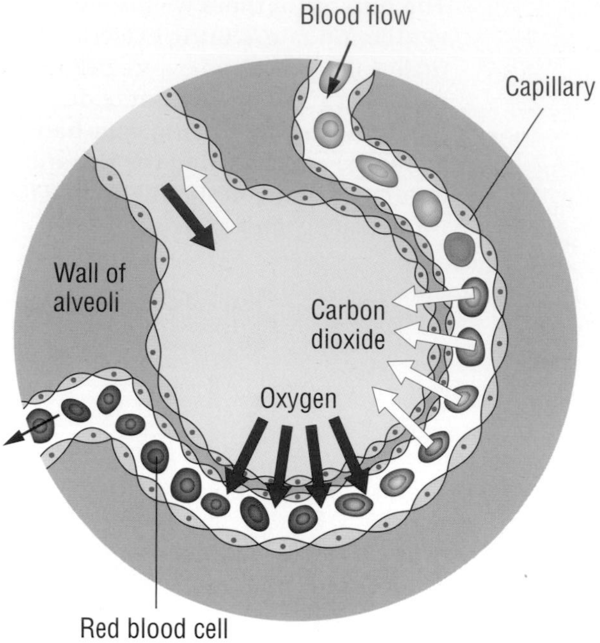

Figure 9.4 Oxygen can be seen leaving the alveolus (singular of alveoli) and carbon dioxide entering from the blood

E QUESTION

From the work you have already completed, you will know that we use oxygen to release energy.

1 What do you think happens to the level of oxygen breathed out, compared with the percentage breathed in?

Carbon dioxide needs to be removed from the body because it is produced during exercise as part of the process that releases energy.

2 What do you think happens to the carbon dioxide levels?
3 Nitrogen is neither used nor created by the body, so what will happen to its levels?
4 Finally, water vapour is released during the process of energy release, therefore what would you expect to happen to the level of water vapour in air that is breathed out?
5 Look at Table 9.1 for a comparison of the values of the gases and water vapour in air that are inspired (breathed in) and expired (breathed out). Does it match your answers?

ACTION 1

Fill in the final column of Table 9.1.

COMPONENT	INSPIRED AIR (%)	EXPIRED AIR (%)	DIFFERENCE	REASON FOR DIFFERENCE
Nitrogen	78	78	Stays the same	
Oxygen	21	17	Drop in value	
Carbon dioxide	0.03	4	Increase in value	
Water vapour	Varies	Saturated	Increase in value	

Table 9.1 Composition of inspired and expired air

Vital capacity
The maximum amount of air that can be expired after a maximal inspiration.

Tidal volume
Movement of air into and out of the lungs in one normal breath.

LUNG VOLUMES

The average adult human can hold about six litres of air in their lungs.

- Tidal volume is the movement of air into and out of the lungs in one normal breath (about half a litre of air).
- Vital capacity is the maximum amount of air that can be expired after a maximal inspiration.

Although the lungs do not respond to regular training, i.e. they do not increase in size, intensive exercise will fatigue the diaphragm and the external intercostal muscles so that they become stronger and more able to cope with the work a sports performer is doing. Due to the increased strength of these muscles, tidal volume can be increased.

E QUESTION

What would you expect to happen to the lines for tidal volume in Figure 9.5 once the performer started to exercise?

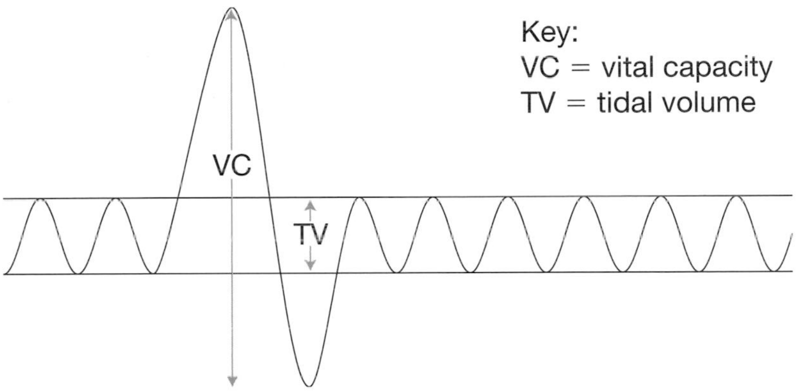

Figure 9.5 Vital capacity and tidal volume of a performer at rest

AEROBIC AND ANAEROBIC RESPIRATION

Aerobic respiration

In this chapter and the last, it has been stated that the body needs oxygen, and more is needed when we exercise. What is the reason for this?

In order for us to do any physical work, we need energy. This energy is released from the food we eat. Energy can be released using oxygen (aerobic) or without using oxygen (anaerobic). More energy is released if oxygen is present, therefore in aerobic activities (remember those? See Chapter 5) the more oxygen supplied to the tissues, the better.

E QUESTION

Are carbohydrates a macronutrient or micronutrient?

Glucose (from carbohydrates) is broken down in our tissues in the presence of oxygen to release energy.

$$\underset{\text{GLUCOSE}}{C_6H_{12}O_6} + \underset{\text{OXYGEN}}{6O_2} \xrightarrow{\text{Gives}} \underset{\text{CARBON DIOXIDE}}{6CO_2} + \underset{\text{WATER}}{6H_2O} + \text{ENERGY}$$

Figure 9.6 Energy equation

ACTION 2

The equation in Figure 9.6 should help explain a lot! Have a look at the equation. Write down any facts which you can work out from it before looking at the list here.

During aerobic respiration:

- energy is released from respiration
- glucose is needed
- oxygen is needed
- carbon dioxide is produced
- water is produced.

By looking at this equation we can see why:

- oxygen levels go down
- carbon dioxide levels go up
- levels of water vapour increase.

We saw from the equation that oxygen is used to release energy. However, if the level of exercise is too intense, oxygen cannot be supplied quickly enough to release energy in this way. When this happens, we release energy anaerobically.

ACTION 3

Shade in the containers of oxygen and carbon dioxide in Figure 9.7 to show what happens to the quantities of these gases as blood circulates around the athlete's body during exercise. The containers are numbered; number 1 is at the lungs, number 2 part way around the circulation and so on until the blood has completed its circuit back to the lungs at number 6.

Figure 9.7 Changing levels of oxygen and carbon dioxide during exercise.

Oxygen debt
The amount of oxygen consumed during recovery above 'normal' due to a shortfall of oxygen during activity.

Questions relating to oxygen debt are often worth more than 1 mark. If any question is worth 2 or more marks, don't forget that you need to write two separate points to gain the extra mark.

Anaerobic respiration

This may last for a short period of time. When we rely on this method of energy release, **lactic acid** is also produced and may then be converted and used as an additional source of energy by the body. The body can not work anaerobically for long periods of time as the body cannot provide energy to the working muscles quickly enough. Muscles also start to fatigue due to the effect of calcium in the muscle. The performer will need time to recover before continuing at the same intensity of physical work. For example, a sprinter doing interval training will complete their sprint and stop, allowing themselves time to recover before completing another set. Games players who have just sprinted for the ball to reach it before their opponent will recover by jogging back into position, once they have passed the ball on. During this recovery period the performer will still be breathing heavily even though they are not working hard. This is so that they can repay the **oxygen debt** they have developed. An oxygen debt is the amount of oxygen consumed during recovery, above that which would normally have been used at rest. It results from a shortfall in availability of oxygen during exercise.

This additional oxygen is used to restock oxygen levels in the muscles and tissues, help replenish energy stores and to help break down any lactic acid that has formed.

E QUESTION

When the athlete finishes his run, will his breathing rate go back to his resting rate straight away? Explain your answer. What is the term used to describe this effect?

IMMEDIATE EFFECTS OF EXERCISE ON THE RESPIRATORY SYSTEM

As soon as you take part in physical activity your body experiences some immediate effects. These are changes that take place on a temporary basis straight away to give immediate help, so that you can complete the work you are asking of your body. Once exercise has stopped your body will slowly return back to its pre-exercise state. The immediate changes to the respiratory system are:

- increased breathing/ventilation rate
- increased depth of breathing rate
- oxygen debt.

EFFECTS OF REGULAR TRAINING ON THE RESPIRATORY SYSTEM

If you continue to exercise on a regular basis, following the principles of training, your body will start to adapt to its increased workload, so that in effect the work becomes easier for the body to do (in other words, you become fitter). These adaptations are what you should refer to if asked about the effects of regular training on the respiratory system:

- increased number of alveoli
- increased strength of diaphragm
- increased strength of the external intercostal muscles
- increased tidal volume.

LONG-TERM HEALTH BENEFITS OF EXERCISE ON THE RESPIRATORY SYSTEM

Changes to the body as a result of regular exercise can also bring about long-term benefits of exercise. The long-term benefit of exercise on the respiratory system is:

- increased efficiency at using oxygen.

THE EFFECTS OF SMOKING ON RESPIRATORY HEALTH

The banning of smoking in public places was brought about due to growing evidence that passive smoking as well as active smoking is harmful to our health. It can lead to:

- lung disease
- lung cancer
- respiratory diseases like emphysema and chronic bronchitis.

Apart from the obvious health risks, smoking will decrease performance in practical activity due to the carbon monoxide contained in cigarette smoke. The haemoglobin in the red blood cells that is normally used to carry oxygen will carry carbon monoxide in preference, reducing the amount of oxygen available to release energy and the performer's ability to work aerobically. Heavy smokers may have as much as ten percent of their haemoglobin bound by carbon monoxide. This obviously has more of an effect on performers in endurance events, but will affect the recovery of all performers. (How many elite 100 metre sprinters do you see smoking?)

CHAPTER 10 A HEALTHY, ACTIVE LIFESTYLE AND YOUR MUSCULAR SYSTEM

GOALS

By the end of this chapter you should be able to:

- explain the role of the muscular system during physical activity
- explain the difference between isometric and isotonic muscle contractions
- describe the immediate and short-term effects of physical activity on the muscular system
- describe the effects of regular exercise and the long-term benefits of physical activity on the muscular system
- identify potential injuries to the muscular system and their common treatment
- explain the advantages and disadvantages of steroid use in relation to muscle building and recovery.

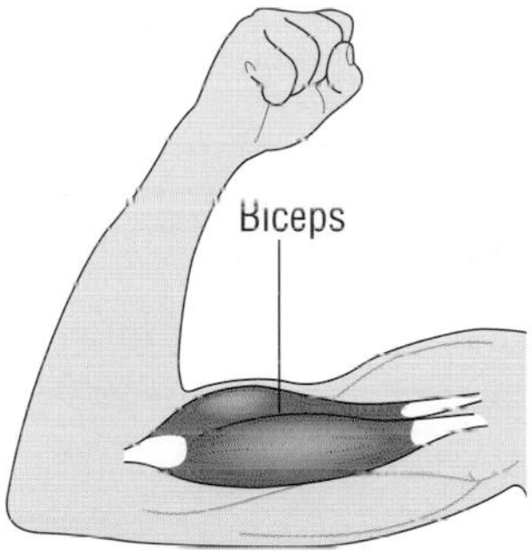

Figure 10.1 The biceps muscle contracts and pulls on the bones of the lower arm

ROLE OF THE MUSCULAR SYSTEM DURING PHYSICAL ACTIVITY

All sports performers need to be able to move. Movement is possible through the use of muscles, but only skeletal muscles bring about movement.

Figure 10.2 shows two volleyball players and a closer look at their muscular system. In order to bring about movement, our muscles contract – they can only pull, not push. They are attached to bones at both ends. One end is fixed and cannot move, so as the muscle contracts, the fixed end (the origin) pulls on the other end of the muscle, which is attached to a different bone. Because this end of the muscle can move (the insertion), it and the bone(s) it is attached to will be pulled towards the other end of the muscle and the bone that is attached to. Look at Figure 10.1 for an example.

The biceps are attached to the scapula (origin) and the radius (insertion). Therefore the end of the muscle near the shoulder does not move, but the other end attached to the lower arm does move. When the muscle contracts, the end at the shoulder stays still, but the end attached to the lower arm moves and brings the bones of the lower arm with it – this is flexion at the elbow.

Antagonistic pair
Two muscles that work together to bring about movement. As one muscle contracts, its opposing muscle relaxes, thus allowing the contracting muscle to pull on the bone. The hamstrings and quadriceps are an example of an antagonistic pair.

Having completed this movement, how do you move your arm back to its original position? A volleyball player smashing the ball will need flexion at the elbow, but then they will need to extend the arm at the elbow to get ready to dig, set or block the opponent's next shot. By relaxing the biceps and contracting the triceps, the triceps pull the lower arm back down to a straight position. Thus there is:

- flexion of the arm at the elbow caused by the biceps and
- extension of the arm at the elbow brought about by the triceps.

The biceps and triceps are working as an antagonistic pair: one muscle contracts while the other relaxes to bring about a movement. The hamstrings and the quadriceps work in the same way.

You should realise that muscle action is complicated, as many muscles often contribute to the action.

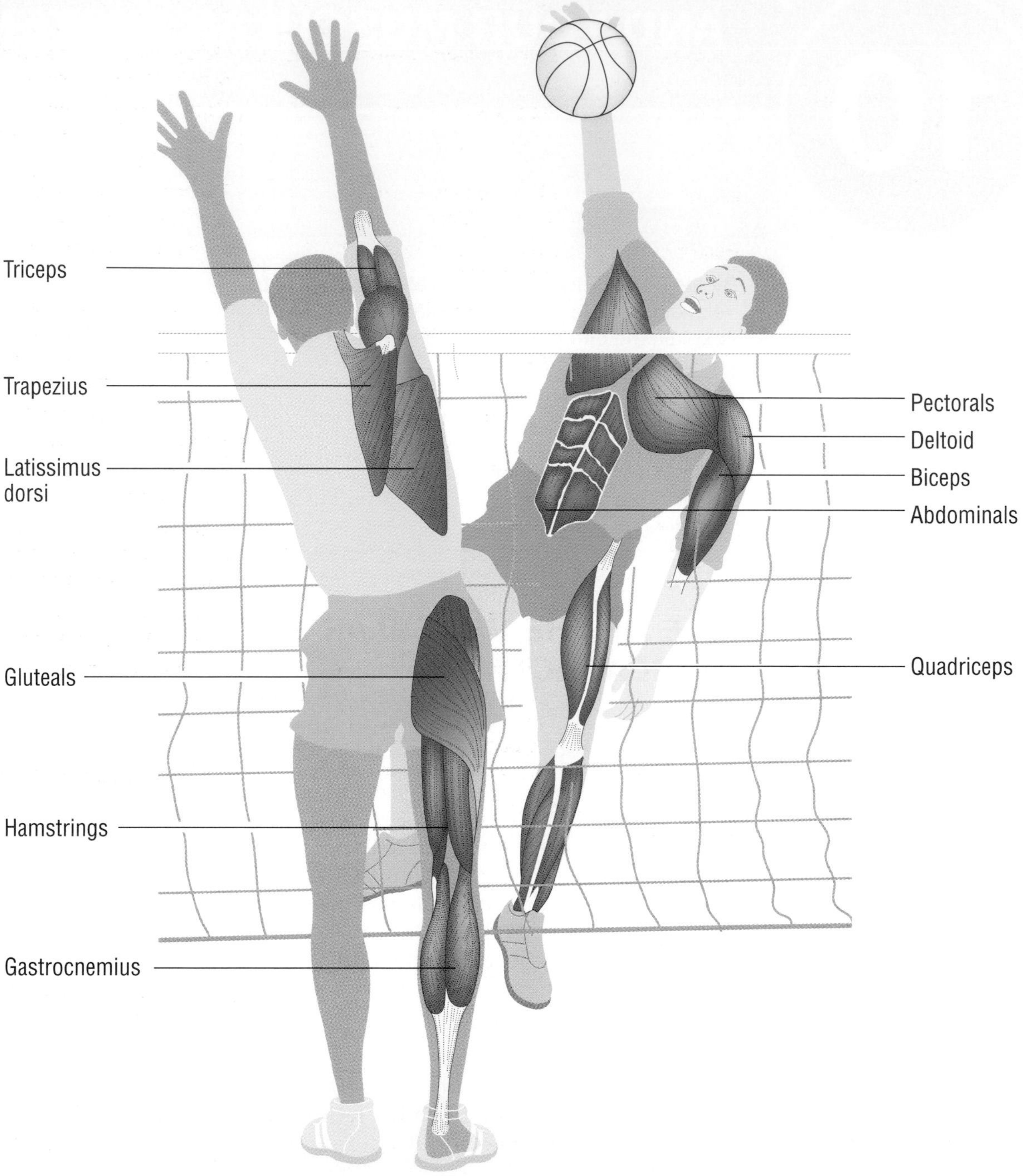

Figure 10.2 The muscular system

E QUESTION

How many of the muscle names in Figure 10.2 do you know already? Do you know what they do? Can you work out what actions they are responsible for from seeing where they are on the images?

ACTION 1

Design a weight training programme or a circuit that will exercise all of the muscles identified in Table 10.1.

MUSCLE	MUSCLE ACTION	SPORTING ACTION
Triceps	Extends lower arm at the elbow	Volleyball player has arms outstretched to block the ball
Biceps	Flexes arm at the elbow	Tennis serve – racket preparation, when racket is behind head
Deltoids	Abducts upper arm at the shoulder	Preparation for a cartwheel in gymnastics
Pectorals	Adduction of upper arm at the shoulder	Arm action in front crawl (pull)
Trapezius	Adducts and rotates scapula, rotation of head at atlas and axis	Lifting of the head to watch the flight of the shuttle in badminton. Back crawl swimming action
Gluteals	Extends the leg at the hip	Running action, one leg is left stretched back behind the other
Quadriceps	Extends the leg at the knee	Follow through after kicking a ball in football
Hamstrings	Flexes the leg at the knee	Tacking the leg back in preparation to strike the ball in a drop goal attempt in rugby
Gastrocnemius	Plantar flexion of the foot (pointing your toes)	Going up onto toes prior to take off in a diving competition
Latissimus dorsi	Adducts and rotates the humerus at the shoulder (draws the arm back and in towards the body)	Pulling the arm back in archery
Abdominals	Flex, rotate and laterally bend trunk	Forward action in sit-ups

Table 10.1 Muscle action and sporting action

ACTION 2

Look at the images in Figure 10.3. Name two of the joints in each image and state the muscle and muscle action that has taken place at that joint.

Figure 10.3 Muscle action at joints in sporting activity

Isotonic and isometric muscle contractions
Isotonic muscle contractions are those contractions which result in visible movement. For example, when the leg muscles contract to allow us to apply a force against the ground so we can move. Isometric contractions are muscle contractions where there is no visible movement.

ISOTONIC AND ISOMETRIC MUSCLE CONTRACTIONS

Muscles contract when they work. The muscle contractions that we have looked at so far have all resulted in movement, and these types of muscle contraction are called isotonic contractions. However, it is possible for a muscle to contract with no resulting movement. These types of contractions are called isometric contractions.

Figure 10.4 Isometric contraction

The only time that muscle contraction will not result in movement is if you are trying to move an immoveable object. For example, if you stand with your arms bent and push them forwards, your arms will move as they straighten. This would be an isotonic contraction. If, however, you repeated this exercise, but pushed against a wall, your arms could not straighten because the wall is immoveable. If you try this you will notice that your muscles are still definitely working, and this is an isometric contraction.

In a tug of war, teams will both pull as hard as each other so both team's muscles are working, but if there is no movement they will be contracting isometrically. During a handstand, muscles are working to maintain the position of the body, but there is no movement – this is another example of an isometric muscle contraction.

E QUESTION
Does your sporting activity use isometric contractions?

E QUESTION
Can you think of any other times in sport where the muscles are working but there is no visible movement?

Figure 10.5 Isometric muscle contraction in limbs where muscles are contracting but there is no movement

IMMEDIATE EFFECTS OF EXERCISE ON THE MUSCULAR SYSTEM

As soon as you take part in physical activity your body experiences some immediate effects. These are changes that take place on a temporary basis straight away to give immediate help, so that you can complete the work you are asking of your body. Once exercise has stopped your body will slowly return back to its pre-exercise state. The immediate changes to the muscular system are:

- increased demand for energy for muscular work
- increased carbon dioxide production
- increased temperature
- lactic acid production during anaerobic work (energy conversion)
- muscle fatigue.

EFFECTS OF REGULAR TRAINING AND THEIR BENEFITS ON THE MUSCULAR SYSTEM

If you continue to exercise on a regular basis, following the principles of training, your body will start to adapt to its increased workload, so that in effect the work becomes easier for the body to do (in other words, you become fitter). These adaptations are what you should refer to if asked about the effects of regular training on the muscular system:

- increased strength of ligaments
- increased strength of tendons
- increased strength of skeletal muscle
- increased size of skeletal muscle (hypertrophy)
- increased mitochondria (site of aerobic respiration)
- increased myoglobin (equivalent to an oxygen 'store' in the muscle).

Although clearly not muscles, ligaments and tendons are soft tissues. Ligaments stabilise joints by joining bone to bone and tendons attach muscle to bone.

POTENTIAL INJURY TO THE MUSCULAR SYSTEM

It is not the intention of the Edexcel exam board that you should administer first aid or become a first aider. You should always seek medical advice if in any doubt about the seriousness of an injury, but if you are involved in sport, it is important that you are able to recognise the signs and symptoms of several types of sports injury. You can use this knowledge if you become injured or if immediate action is needed in the case of an emergency. The information that follows is a basic understanding of the conditions and procedures. More detailed information can be obtained from organisations such as the St John Ambulance.

Soft tissue injuries

Bone is made of a hard material, therefore anything that is not bone is called soft tissue. This refers to muscles, ligaments and tendons.

Soft tissue injuries are common in sport. In athletics it is not unusual to see an athlete suddenly pull out of a race holding their hamstrings because of a strained (torn or pulled) muscle. This usually happens when a muscle is stretched beyond its limits and normally occurs where the tendon joins the muscle.

Another soft tissue injury is deep bruising. Deep bruising is a bruise of the muscle rather than the skin.

Symptoms

STRAINS	DEEP BRUISING
Pain	Pain
Visible bruising	Swelling
	Limited range of movement

Treatment

Soft tissue injuries should be treated using the RICE procedure:

- **R** Rest – take a break from the activity. A doctor, nurse or physiotherapist suggest how long you should rest based on the severity of the injury.
- **I** Ice – apply ice to the injured part (although not directly onto the skin).
- **C** Compression – a bandage is wrapped around the injured part to reduce further swelling and to give support.
- **E** Elevation – lift the injured part. This reduces blood flow to the injury, reducing the amount of bruising.

E QUESTION

Which training principle relates to the loss of fitness due to lack of training?

If the injuries resulted in time away from regular training, muscles would re-adapt to their new level of activity and the adaptations described above would begin to be lost. When a muscle decreases in size it is called muscular **atrophy**. Gently easing back into trainning after a period of inactivity will result in the body readapting.

E QUESTION

Which training principle should be applied when 'easing back into training' after a period of inactivity?

PERFORMANCE ENHANCING DRUGS – USE OF STEROIDS

Remember that anabolic steroids do not increase muscle bulk on their own; they allow the performer to train harder so, as a result of the increased intensity of training, muscles will adapt and increase in size.

More information is given about this topic in Chapter 7. We are just concerned here with the specific class of drug that has a significant effect on the muscular system.

Anabolic steroids such as testosterone or nandrolone are taken for their effect on skeletal muscle. The drug allows the performer to build up muscle size and strength. However, according to the Austrialian Sports Anti-Doping Authority (ASADA) Nov 2008, nandrolone's reputation for easing the pain and strain caused by intensive training, or hasten recovery from injury, is not scientifically based.

Testosterone is a hormone that occurs naturally in the body, but nandrolone is a synthetic drug.

There are many good reasons for not taking steroids apart from the fact it is illegal in sport. There are many harmful side effects linked to this class of drugs, for example, liver/kidney damage, an increase in aggressive behaviour, acne, low sperm count in men and premature heart disease.

REST

Rest is required for adaptations to training to take place, the muscular system needs time to recover before working hard agin. The principles of rest and recovery can be found in Chapter 4.

DIET

Following a balanced diet is very important for elite sports performer. Correct balance of protein, for example, is essential for growth and repair of muscle. More information can be found on this topic in Chapter 6.

CHAPTER 11 AN ACTIVE, HEALTHY LIFESTYLE AND YOUR SKELETAL SYSTEM

GOALS

By the end of this chapter you should be able to:

- describe the role of the skeletal system during physical activity
- describe the effects of regular exercise and the long-term benefits of physical activity on the skeletal system
- recognise the importance of weight-bearing exercise and an appropriate diet to reduce likelihood of osteoporosis
- identify potential injuries to the skeletal system and their common treatment.

http://videos.howstuffworks.com/hsw/25404-human-body-the-skeletal-system-video.htm
Short introduction to the functions of the skeleton.

http://videos.howstuffworks.com/hsw/16795-the-skeletal-and-muscular-systems-care-of-the-systems-video.htm
Short overview of the need for correct diet in relation to skeletal maintenance.

What does the skeleton do? The skeleton:

- **gives the body its shape and supports us in an upright position**. This is vital for sporting performance.
- **protects the body's vital organs**. The role of the skeleton to protect vital organs is very important in sport. For example, the ribs and sternum protect the heart and lungs if a batsman is struck with a cricket ball, the cranium protects the brain from head injury in rugby during tackles or racket injury in squash (if the opposition has a wide swing); the pelvic girdle protects the intestines if there is a misplaced punch in boxing.
- **allows movement through the use of joints and muscle attachment**. Most sports involve a lot of movement; e.g. squash, football and netball would be impossible to play if we were unable to use any of our muscles to move our bones.

We have over 200 bones in our bodies; fortunately, you do not have to know all of their names!

ACTION 1

Once you have become familiar with the names of these bones, copy each of their names onto sticky labels and place them on a friend to help reinforce your understanding of the correct location of each bone.

Although you will not be asked to label a skeleton, you will need to know the names of bones forming joints and moved by muscles.

THE BONES OF THE SKELETON NE

Figure 11.1 shows the major bones of the human skeleton.

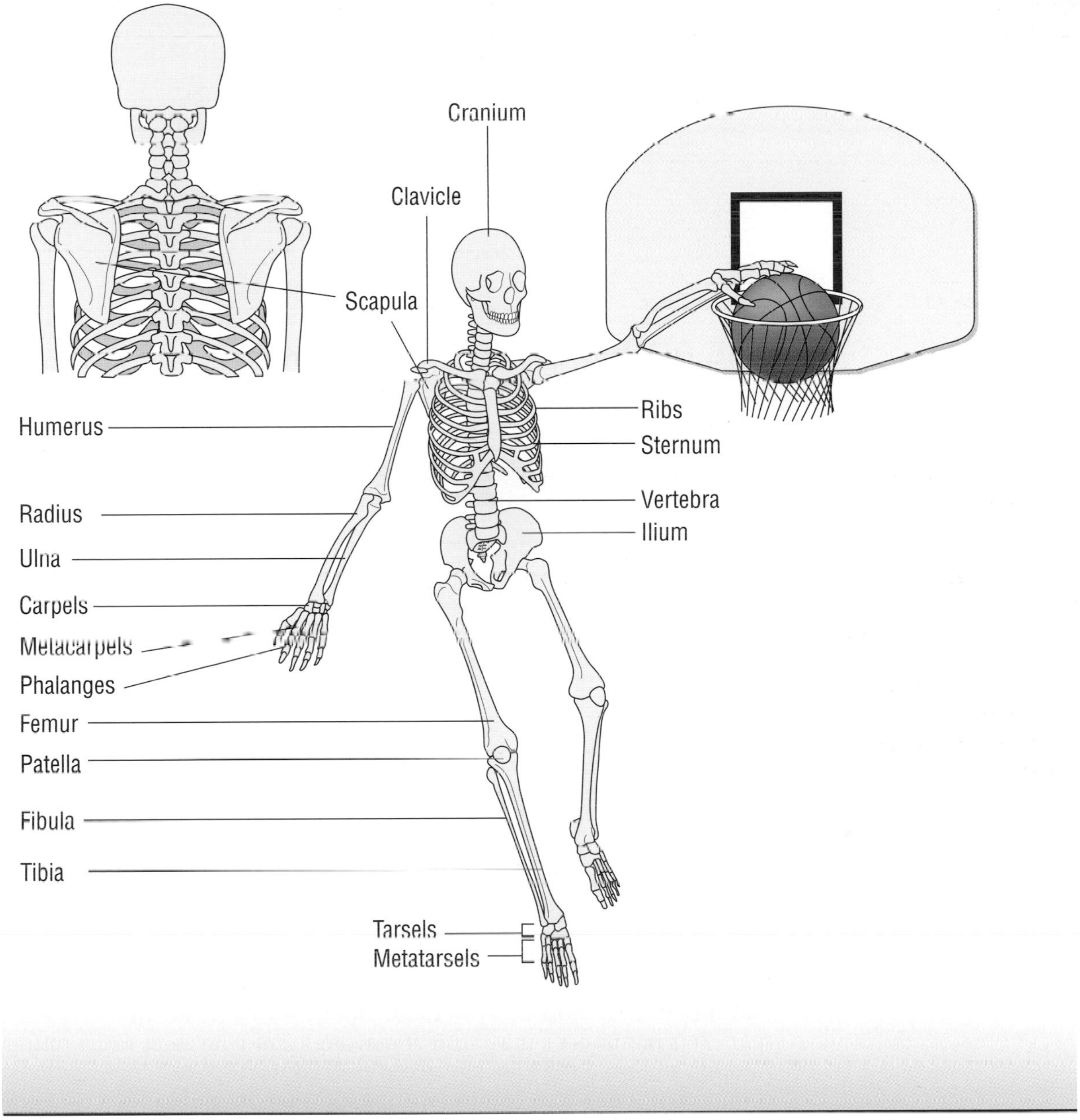

Figure 11.1 The human skeleton NE

ACTION 2 NE

Using Figure 11.1, identify the occasions where two or more bones meet.

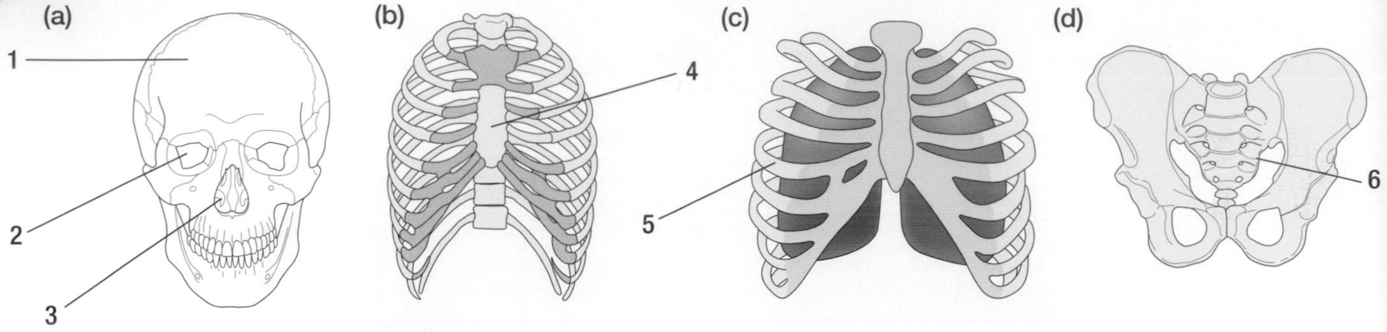

Figure 11.2 The skeleton as protector

THE BONES OF THE ELBOW, KNEE, HIP AND SHOULDER (NE)

ACTION 3

Look at the images in Figure 11.2. Which organs would be protected by the bones of the skeleton indicated by the numbered lines 1–6?

ACTION 4 (NE)

Use the images of the skeleton to help you fill in the empty column in Table 11.1. List the bones that make the joint.

NAME OF JOINT	BONES THAT MAKE UP THE JOINT
Elbow	
Shoulder	
Hip	
Knee	
Neck	

Table 11.1 Bones and joints

Check your answers with those in Table 11.2. It is possible that you might have added a couple of extra bones to some of the joints. Only the bones that actually articulate (meet) with each other form the joint.

The shoulder joint is the most freely moveable in the body. This obviously presents an advantage in terms of sport – look at the arm action in the butterfly stroke for swimming, or the bowling action in cricket, both demand a high level of mobility. You cannot achieve this amount of movement with any other limb. The disadvantage is that it is a relatively unstable joint, i.e. it can dislocate.

The knee joint is most likely to cause problems in later life due to overuse in sport. It is put under a great deal of pressure from pounding when running and turning, and from the knocks it receives in contact sports. Knee injuries are most common in sports that require twisting movements and sudden changes of direction, e.g. football, rugby, basketball, netball and skiing.

CLASSIFICATION OF JOINTS

You should be able to classify the joints listed in Table 11.1 as either:

- hinge (elbow and knee)
- pivot (atlas and axis) (NE)
- ball and socket (hip and shoulder).

Joints are classified into certain types depending on the amount of movement that can be carried out; e.g. the movement possible at your knee is different from the movement possible at the shoulder.

MOVEMENT AT JOINTS

The reason you need to know that there are different types of joints is that the type of joint will determine the type of movement we can do at that joint.

NAME OF JOINT	BONES THAT MAKE UP THE JOINT	IMAGE OF THE JOINT
Elbow	Humerus, radius and ulna (Joint 1) and radius and ulna (Joint 2)	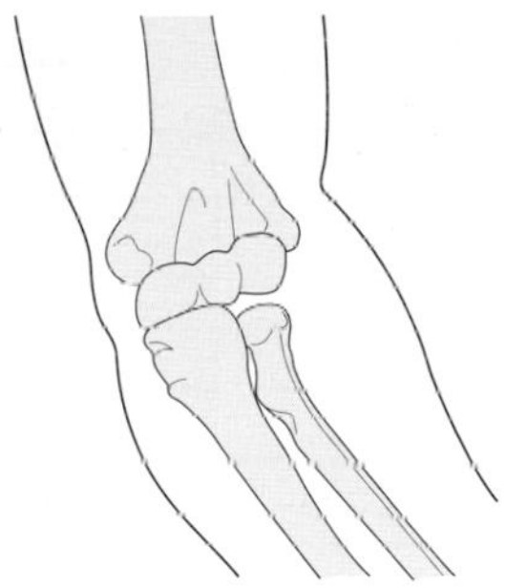
Shoulder	Humerus Scapula	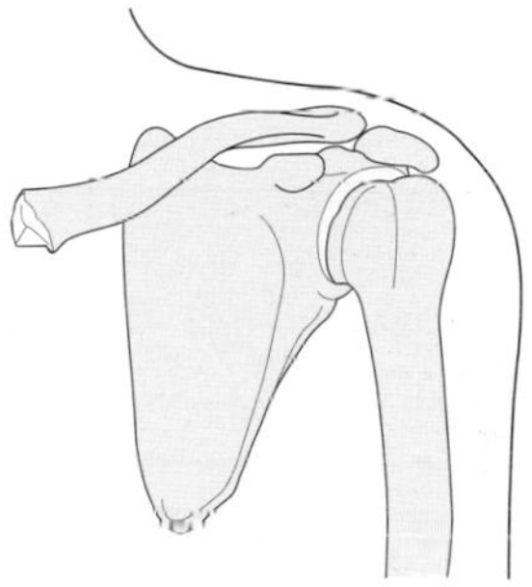
Hip	Femur Hip (the fused bones of the ilium, ischium and pubis)	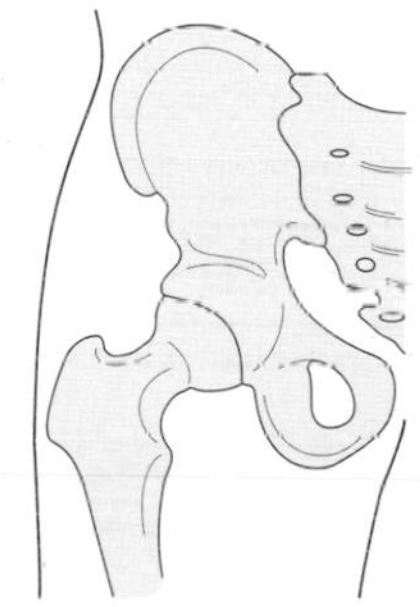
Knee	Femur Tibia (Although the fibula is next to the tibia it is not involved in the movement at the joint. Similarly, the patella is there to protect the front of the joint)	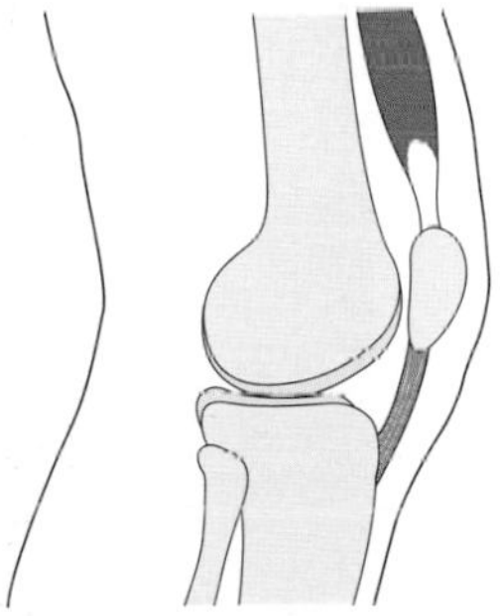
Neck	Atlas Axis (This is the name commonly given to this joint rather than neck)	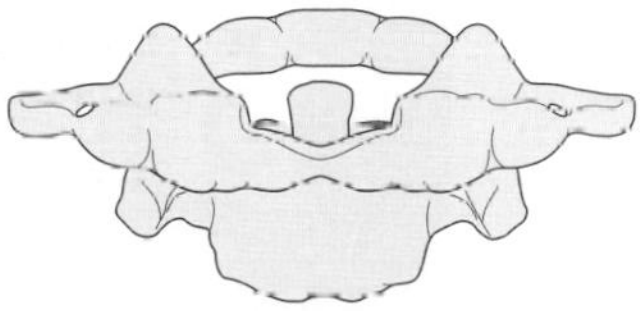

Table 11.2 Bones and joints

Movements at joints are known as joint actions and are given specific names, as shown in Table 11.3.

JOINT ACTION	DESCRIPTION OF ACTION	EXAMPLE FROM SPORT	EXPLANATION
Flexion	Bending a limb at a joint	Dribbling a ball in basketball	The elbow of the ball-handler is bent when dribbling a ball
Extension	Straightening a limb at a joint	A discus thrower during their spin	The arm holding the discus is straight
Abduction	Movement of a limb sideways away from the centre of the body	A gymnast performing a straddle position	The gymnast's legs have been moved sideways away from the centre of the body
Adduction	Movement of a limb sideways towards the centre of the body	A gymnast moving from a straddle to straight position	The gymnast's legs have moved together
Rotation	Circular movement around the joint	A swimmer in a race	The swimmer's arms make a circular action to complete the butterfly stroke

Table 11.3 Joint actions

You can see examples of the different joint actions every time you watch a sports performer. The athlete in Figure 11.2 is straightening his arm as he begins to pull the paddle back through the water. He is therefore extending (joint action) the arm at the elbow (joint).

Figure 11.2 Joint action in sport

ACTION 5

From the information in this chapter you should be able to answer the following true or false questions. Not all of this knowledge will be examined.

True or false?

1. The elbow is a hinge joint.
2. The knee is a pivot joint.
3. The elbow is a pivot joint.
4. The shoulder is a pivot joint.
5. The elbow allows flexion and extension.
6. The elbow allows abduction.
7. The hip is a ball and socket joint.
8. The atlas and axis can rotate because they are a hinge joint.
9. All joint actions are possible at the elbow.
10. All joint actions are possible at the hip.
11. The knee is a hinge joint.
12. The atlas and axis can rotate because they are a pivot joint.
13. The shoulder is a ball and socket joint and can rotate.
14. The hip has more movement possibilities that the knee.
15. The elbow has more movement possibilities than the knee.

ACTION 6

Name the joint and the joint action occurring at A and B in Figures 11.3 and 11.4.

Figure 11.3 Joint action in high jump

Figure 11.4 Joint action in archery

ACTION	ACTION AT THE JOINT

Table 11.4 Joint actions

ACTION 7

Try to name some of the joint actions occurring at the knee, elbow and shoulder for the sporting skills/techniques shown in Table 11.5. You may find it easier to work with a partner – one of you can mime the action, while the other analyses the movement – once finished compare your answers with others.

SKILL/TECHNIQUE	JOINT	JOINT ACTION
Sprint start ('Set')	Knee	
	Elbow	
Stationary, inverted position in a handstand	Knee	
	Elbow	
Kicking the ball in football	Knee	
	Elbow	
Bowling the ball in cricket	Shoulder	
Completing a cartwheel	Elbow	
	Shoulder	

Table 11.5 Joint actions

ACTION 8

Create a revision table by filling in the information missing from Table 11.6.

JOINT NAME	JOINT TYPE	JOINT ACTION	EXAMPLE FROM SPORT
Knee			
Elbow			
Shoulder			
Atlas, axis			

Table 11.6 Revision table

HOMEWORK

Take a photograph of youself performing in sport or taking part in a PE lesson (or use a suitable image from a newspaper). Print your photograph and stick it in the centre of a piece of plain paper. Choose two joints that you are using in the picture and draw a small box around them as shown in Figure 11.5. On your paper, draw the bones as they would appear in the joint, label them, state the name and type of the joint and the action that is happening at the joint in the photograph.

Figure 11.5 Joint action in racket sport

EFFECTS OF REGULAR TRAINING AND THEIR BENEFITS ON THE SKELETAL SYSTEM

Bones are living tissue. They reshape and rebuild themselves many times as you grow, age and exercise and your diet will affect them.

As a result of taking part in weight-bearing exercise such as walking, running and games such as tennis or aerobics on a regular basis, your body will start to adapt to its increased workload. These adaptations are what you should refer to if asked about the effects of regular training on the skeletal system:

- increased bone density
- increased strength of bones which results in a reduction in the risk of osteoporosis.

> **Osteoporosis**
> A disease of the bone which leads to increased risk of fracture.

Osteoporosis is a disease of bone that leads to an increased risk of fracture. Although normally associated with older people it can affect those in their 20s, and can have a very negative impact on an individual's quality of life. Imagine breaking a bone everytime you fell over, or cracking a rib because you coughed too hard when you had a cold. Calcium and vitamin D can help to increase bone density so they should be an important part of your diet. Calcium is stored in bone and makes it hard, but if you do not get enough calcium from your daily diet, your body will 'steal' the calcium from your bones to use for other functions. This can reduce your bone strength and lead to osteoporosis. Vitamin D is important because this helps the body to absorb the calcium you eat. Vitamin D can be made by the body when the skin is in sunlight.

POTENTIAL INJURY TO THE SKELETAL SYSTEM

Fractures

A fracture is a break or crack in a bone. Fractures occur as a result of direct or indirect force. As a result, they tend to be associated with contact sports. For example, fractures of bones in the lower leg and foot can happen in football as a result of direct force, i.e. being kicked. An example of an indirect force causing a fracture is when players fall and put their arms out to break their fall. The point of impact is at the wrist/hand, but the force travels along the arm to the shoulder and onto the clavicle, which can then fracture. Fractures can be:

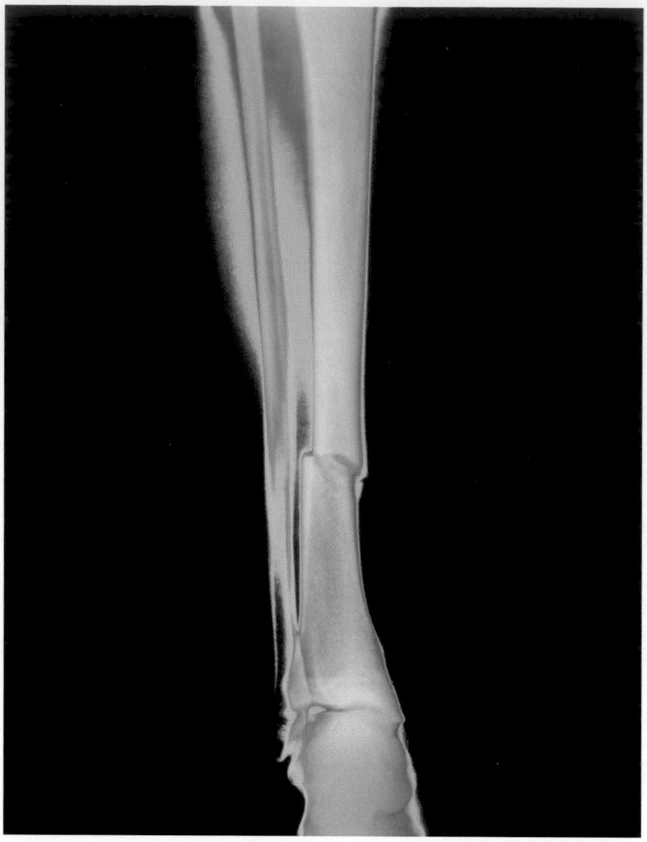

Figure 11.6 An X-ray of a fractured bone in the leg

Compound – these are also known as open fractures where the bone breaks the skin.
Greenstick – this tends to happen in young children as the bone bends rather than breaks.
Simple – a fracture that does not break the skin.
Stress – this type of fracture is a common sports injury. Unlike the other types of fracture it is associated with overuse. It is also called a hairline fracture as it is normally a very thin crack in the bone.

Symptoms

Symptoms of fractures include:

- difficulty in moving the injured limb
- pain
- distortion of 'natural' shape
- swelling
- bruising.

JOINT INJURIES

There are different types of joint injury that you could be asked questions about.

Dislocation

Dislocations occur at joints, where the bone is moved out of its normal position. Dislocations as a result of sports injuries tend to happen at the shoulder, thumb and finger. They occur as a result of a heavy force acting on the joint; e.g. diving to score a try in rugby and falling on the shoulder.

Symptoms

These include:

- pain
- distortion of 'natural' shape.

Tennis elbow

This is an injury to the muscles of the forearm that allow you to extend your wrist and turn your palm upward, and the tendon that attaches the muscle to the elbow joint. It is called tennis elbow because the injury is common in tennis – the action of extending your wrist and turning your palm upward is carried out when you play a backhand stroke.

Poor technique or the wrong size of grip on a racket can cause tennis elbow because of the unnecessary force acting on the tissues.

Figure 11.7 Action of hitting the ball can cause tennis elbow

Symptoms

These include:

- pain (on the outside of the arm and elbow)
- stiffness at the elbow joint.

Golfer's elbow

This affects the muscles and tendons responsible for flexing the wrist, and is an injury caused by overuse. The injury is referred to as golfer's elbow because it is associated with that sport.

During a game, golfers need to bend the wrist repeatedly when striking the ball. This can result in golfer's elbow if players play too much. You can develop tennis elbow or golfer's elbow even if you do not play those sports.

Figure 11.8 Golfer's elbow can be caused through playing golf

Symptoms

These include:

- pain around the elbow joint, normally on the inside of the joint.

Look for the common symptoms of sports injury and make sure you remember those as you will be able to apply them to a variety of specific injuries.

Cartilage tear

A torn cartilage at the knee is another joint injury. The cartilage normally fits on the ends of the bones of the knee joint, but if the cartilage is damaged or begins to deteriorate with age, it can tear. The torn piece of cartilage moves in the joint and can become caught or wedged between the bones. If this happens, the knee becomes painful, difficult to move and swollen.

Symptoms

These include:

- pain around the knee joint
- swollen knee
- difficulty in moving.

E QUESTION

What do the letters RICE stand for?

Twisted ankle/sprain

A twisted ankle is also a joint injury, but as it is caused by wrenching or twisting of a ligament it is also considered to be a soft tissue injury. The symtoms are very similar to other soft tissue injuries:

- pain around the joint
- swelling
- visible brusing.

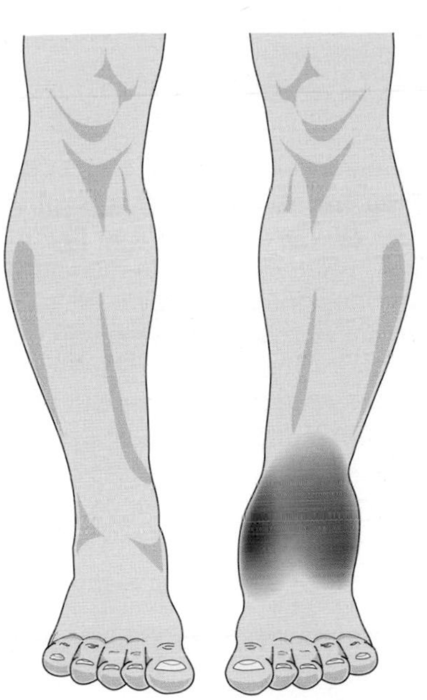

Figure 11.9 Note the bruising and swelling at the ankle as a result of a sprain

As with other soft tissue injuries sprains should be treated using the RICE procedure.

ACTION 9

Fill in the blanks. The missing words are all in Table 11.7.

A is a break or crack in a bone. Apart from pain, two other symptoms of this injury are ______________________ and ______________________ .
This is the type of fracture where the bone bends rather than breaks. ______________________ .
The pain from golfer's elbow is normally felt on the ______________________ of the joint.
The pain associated with torn cartilage is due to the cartilage in the joint.
Strains and ______________________ are soft tissue injuries.
You can strain a muscle or a ______________________ .
Another type of soft tissue injury is ______________________ bruising.
______________________ is a symptom of a soft tissue injury.
All soft tissue injuries should be treated using the ______________________ procedure.

Moving	Greenstick	Swelling	RICE
Pain	Deep	Tendon	Fracture
Bruising	Inside	Elbow	Sprains

Table 11.7 Factors that contribute to sports injuries

ACTION 10

In teams, number yourselves from one to four. Take it in turns to collect a sports injury card from the front of the class. DO NOT tell anyone else your injury (if you do, you lose the point and the other teams gain one). Think about the symptoms of the injury and mime these to your group. Your group are allowed a maximum of TWO attempts to state the injury based on your mime of the symptoms. If they guess correctly they then have to say what a first aider would do if they came across someone who had that sports injury.

Your team scores one point for correctly guessing the injury and one point for each correct action carried out by the first aider. Once you have had your go, the next team member collects a card.

Some sample cards are shown in Figure 11.10. Create some more in your team and add them to those made by the other teams in your class.

Figure 11.10 Sample sports injury cards

DIET AND THE SKELETAL SYSTEM

Calcuim and vitamin D are essential for bone gowth and 'health'. Additional information relating to the importance of diet can be found in Chapter 6.

CHAPTER 12 TESTING YOUR UNDERSTANDING

Check with your teacher about the course you are following. If at the time of writing you are following the short course you will not need to answer questions on Chapters 7–11. You will also be answering a mainly multiple choice paper, but ask your teacher, as sometimes these things change! Work through the relevant questions to you, i.e. only those from the chapters you need to kow, but attempt both full and short course questions (it is good practice). Once you can answer all of the relevant questions in this chapter you will be very well-prepared for your final exam. There is a crossword to finish the chapter.

CHAPTER 1 (HEALTHY, ACTIVE LIFESTYLES AND HOW THEY COULD BENEFIT YOU)

1 Peter is 16 years old. Although he has always enjoyed PE, he is very shy and overweight.
Complete the table below stating THREE possible benefits to Peter of joining a sports club. Explain how joining a club may achieve these benefits.
(Total 6 marks)

	BENEFIT	HOW ACHIEVED
1		
2		
3		

Table 12.1

Questions 2 to 5 relate to the categories of benefits of physical activity.
The possible benefits of taking part in exercise can be grouped:
A Mental
B Physical
C Social
D Aesthetic
Which of the benefits of exercise named above, A, B, C or D, would best match each of the following statements in questions 2 to 5?

2 I participate in exercise to relieve stress. (1 mark)

3 I joined a local sports club so that I could get out more and meet people. (1 mark)

4 By taking part in dance I am able to appreciate the skill involved and have become more creative and able to express my ideas. (1 mark)

5 I re-started my training after Christmas to try to lose some of my excess weight. (1 mark)

CHAPTER 2 (INFLUENCES ON YOUR HEALTHY, ACTIVE LIFESTYLE)

1 Jan is a good all-round sports performer and could represent the school in many different sports but has chosen swimming.
Explain how her family and their socio-economic status may influence her choice of sporting activity. (2 marks)

2 Figure 12.1 shows the sports participation pyramid.
Name and describe the stage labelled 1. (2 marks)

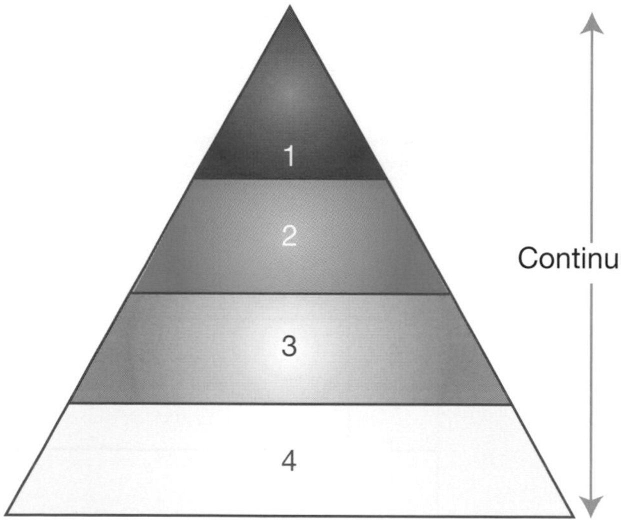

Figure 12.1 The Participation Pyramid

3 Which of the following is a correct statement in relation to Sport England's Start, Stay, Succeed objectives?

A Start – plan so that every child starts the school day with physical activity to increase participation and improve health.
B Start – increase the number of adults who start their day with exercise.
C Stay – aim to keep officials working in sport so that development costs are reduced.
D Succeed – create opportunities for talented performers to achieve success.

4 Name three initiatives that have been developed to provide opportunities for becoming, or remaining, involved in physical activity. (3 marks)

CHAPTER 3 (EXERCISE AND FITNESS AS PART OF YOUR HEALTHY, ACTIVE LIFESTYLE)

Use the following to answer questions 1 to 3.

The following are all areas of fitness.

A Muscular strength
B Muscular endurance
C Flexibility
D Cardiovascular fitness

Figure 12.2 shows a badminton player playing a shot.

Figure 12.2 A badminton player reaching for a shot

1 Which area of fitness helps the player stretch to reach the shuttlecock? (1 mark)

2 Which area of fitness combines with speed to provide the power in the player's shots? (1 mark)

3 Which area of fitness allows the player to continue to use his arm muscles during long rallies without the muscles becoming fatigued? (1 mark)

4 a) Give one reason why a person may be physically fit but still considered to be unhealthy. (1 mark)

b) Give the correct term for 'how well a task is completed'. (1 mark)

c) Exercise is 'a form of physical activity done to maintain or improve health and/or physical fitness, it is not competitive sport'. How might exercise improve health and fitness? (2 marks)

Figure 12.3 shows performers participating in physical activity.

Figure 12.3 Using skill-related fitness

5 Complete Table 12.2 naming ONE component of skill-related fitness that will be important to each performer. Explain how these components will help each performer in his/her activity. You must choose a different component for each performer. (Total 6 marks)

PERFORMER	COMPONENT OF SKILL-RELATED FITNESS	HOW COMPONENT OF SKILL-RELATED FITNESS HELPS PERFORMANCE
Gymnast		
Sprinter		
Shot putter		

Table 12.2

The following are all areas of skill-related fitness.

A Co-ordination
B Reaction time
C Speed
D Power

The following statements in questions 6 to 9 explain how Ashley, a 100 metre sprinter, uses all of the areas of skill-related fitness, A, B, C and D. Match each statement with the correct area of skill-releated fitness.

6 To help him drive out of the starting blocks at the start of the race. (1 mark)

7 To use his arms and legs together to create a better running action. (1 mark)

8 To make sure he leaves the blocks as soon as possible after the gun has sounded. (1 mark)

9 To complete a race faster than his opponent. (1 mark)

CHAPTER 4 (PHYSICAL ACTIVITY AS PART OF YOUR HEALTHY, ACTIVE LIFESTYLE (PART 1))

1 If you are normally inactive what should you complete before undertaking a significant increased physical workload? (1 mark)

2 Fitness tests are often used to provide data about current levels of fitness before planning a fitness programme. Name three fitness tests and the aspect of fitness they measure. (6 marks)

3 To improve performance, athletes often work on their fitness. In order to be effective, performers should devise a Personal Exercise Programme (PEP). Hope is 16, and plays sport at a good standard. The following is an extract of some of her thoughts about her PEP:

At present I am training three times a week, every week. I use a different method of training for each session, but I make sure that I focus on appropriate tasks for my activity. At the end of each session I plan the next one, gradually increasing the amount of work I do when I think it is getting too easy. My PEP is different to the other players in the team.

a) From the extract state four Principles of Training that Hope applies:
(i)
(ii)
(iii)
(iv) (4 marks)

b) For each Principle of Training that you have identified, give an example from the extract to support your answer. (4 marks)

c) Why does Hope design her own PEP rather than using the same programme as one of her friends? (1 mark)

(Total 9 marks)

Use the statements below to answer questions 4 to 6.

The following statements all relate to the FITT principle.

A How hard you work.
B Making sure that your training matches the needs of your sport.
C How long each training session lasts.
D How often you train.

4 Which of these statements is referring to Frequency?

5 Which of these statements is referring to Type?

6 Which of these statements is referring to Intensity? (3 marks)

Use the statements below to answer questions 7 to 9.

The following statements are taken from a GCSE PE student's Personal Exercise Programme (PEP).

A I found the workload far too easy last week so I shall be training harder this week.
B I think it is important to gradually increase the amount of work that I do.
C I need to structure my PEP to my needs, no-one else's.
D Unfortunately I had to have a minor operation on my knee. I was unable to train for six weeks, which means that I have already started to lose my fitness.

7 Which statement refers to the principle of progresive overload?

8 Which statement refers to the principle of reversibility? (2 marks)

9 Explain the link between the principles of rest and recovery. (2 marks)

CHAPTER 5 (PHYSICAL ACTIVITY AS PART OF YOUR HEALTHY, ACTIVE LIFESTYLE (PART 2))

1 Fartlek, circuit, weight and interval are all types of training methods.

a) Briefly describe each type of training method.

Fartlek:
Circuit:
Weight:
Interval: (4 marks)

b) Look at the following list of sporting performers.

Hockey player	Football midfield player
Tennis player	Competitive swimmer
Shot putter	Rower
Sprinter	Netball shooter

Complete Table 12.3 by selecting the most appropriate performer from the list above for each type of training. Each performer may only be used once.
(4 marks)

TYPE OF TRAINING	SPORTS PERFORMER
Fartlek	
Circuit	
Weight	
Interval	

Table 12.3

TYPE OF TRAINING	VALUE OF TRAINING METHOD TO SPORTING ACTIVITY
Fartlek	
Circuit	
Weight	
Interval	

Table 12.4

c) Complete Table 12.4 by explaining why the training method is of value to the sports performer that you have chosen. (4 marks)
(Total 12 marks)

Figure 12.4 shows a record of Jane's heart rate before, during and after a training session.

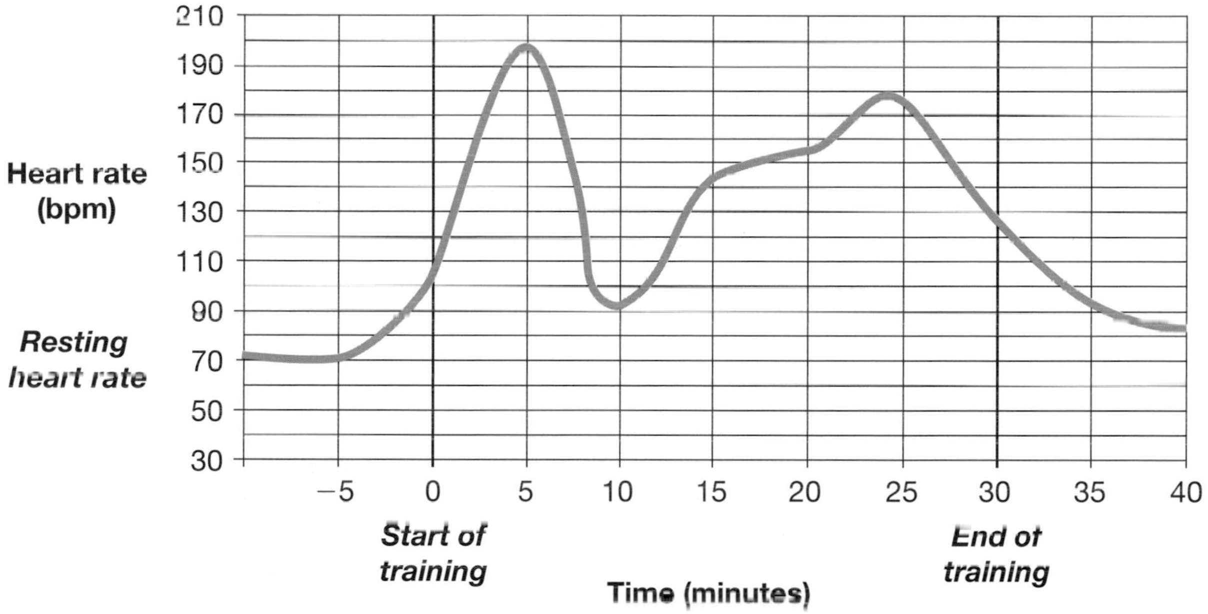

Figure 12.4 Heart rate values before and after a training session

Questions 2 to 4 relate to the information in Figure 12.4.

2 Why does Jane's heart rate drop during the training session?
A She becomes tired.
B She increases her workload.
C She decreases her workload.
D She maintains the same workload. (1 mark)

3 How long does it take Jane to recover?
A She recovers immediately.
B One minute.
C Less than 5 minutes.
D More than 5 minutes. (1 mark)

4 If Jane's target heart rate training zones were to be added to the graph, what percentages of her maximum heart rate should be used to calculate her target heart rate training zones?
A 50% and 60%.
B 55% and 65%.
C 60% and 80%.
D 70% and 100%. (1 mark)

CHAPTER 6 (YOUR PERSONAL HEALTH AND WELL-BEING)

The following should all be present in a balanced diet.

A Protein
B Fats
C Carbohydrates
D Water

1 Which of these provides energy for anaerobic respiration? (1 mark)

2 Which of these are required to reduce the chances of becoming dehydrated? (1 mark)

3 a) In addition to keeping fit, Ashan knows that it is important to consider what and how much he eats.
Why would Ashan include the following in his diet?
i) Carbohydrates (1 mark)
ii) Protein (1 mark)

4 What happens to blood flow to the digestive system during exercise? (1 mark)

5 Why does the change in blood flow to the digestive system mean that you should not eat within two hours of moderate to high intensity exercise? (1 mark)

The remaining questions (Chapter 7 to 11) are for full-course students only.

CHAPTER 7 (PHYSICAL ACTIVITY AND YOUR HEALTHY MIND AND BODY)

Questions 1 to 3 relate to the four statements below.

The following should all be present in a balanced diet:

A Protein
B Fats
C Carbohydrates
D Water

1 If eaten in excess, which of these is most likely to lead to obesity? (1 mark)

2 Why is it important that Ashan does not undereat? (1 mark)

3 It is important that Ashan does not overeat. Explain the term overeat. (1 mark)

4 Which of these is a possible side-effect of taking narcotic analgesics?

A Dehydration
B Acne
C Increased chance of injury
D Increased chance of heart disease (1 mark)

5 What is the purpose of 'balancing competition'?
A To see which gymnastics team can hold a position for the longest.
B To try to even out sides within a competition.
C To make sure that the cost of running a competition does not exceed the money generated from ticket sales.
D To see which gymnast can use the most balances within their competition routine. (1 mark)

Questions 6 to 8 relate to the following four statements.
A As I arrived late I had no time to warm up properly.
B I made sure I remembered my shin pads for this game.
C Before making the substitution the referee checked the studs on my boots to make sure they were not too long or made of metal.
D After the match I made sure I had a shower before going home. (1 mark)

6 Which statement should reduce the chance of injury to an opponent?

7 Which statement should reduce the chance of injury to the football player? (1 mark)

8 a) One way of attempting to prevent injury is to 'play by the rules'. Complete Table 12.5 by giving two examples from a sporting activity of your choice to show how 'rules' may prevent injury.
ACTIVITY: ______________ (2 marks)

	DESCRIPTION OF RULE	HOW RULE REDUCES CHANCE OF INJURY
1		
2		

Table 12.5

b) i) Different activities create different levels of risk for the performers. Which of the following activities presents the greatest risk? (1 mark)
Basketball; Weight training; 1500m; Rock climbing
ii) Explain your answer. (1 mark)
c) Complete Table 12.6 by giving a potential risk, and a precaution that could be taken to reduce that risk. Each risk and precaution may only be used once. (8 marks)
(Total 12 marks)

ACTIVITY	POTENTIAL RISK	MEASURE TO REDUCE RISK
Basketball		
Weight training		
1500m		
Rock climbing		

Table 12.6

CHAPTER 8 (A HEALTHY, ACTIVE LIFESTYLE AND YOUR CARDIOVASCULAR SYSTEM)

1 Stroke volume is:

A The amount of blood ejected from the heart per minute.
B The number of times the heart beats per minute.
C The amount of blood ejected from the heart per beat.
D The pace-maker responsible for timing the stroke of the heart. (1 mark)

2 i) What long-term effect would aerobic training have on Ria's resting heart rate and stroke volume?

Heart rate ______________________________ (1 mark)

Stroke volume ______________________________ (1 mark)

ii) Identify another effect that training could have on Ria's heart.

______________________________ (1 mark)

(Total 3 marks)

CHAPTER 9 (A HEALTHY, ACTIVE LIFESTYLE AND YOUR RESPIRATORY SYSTEM)

1 Vital capacity is:

A The amount of air breathed in and out during normal breathing.
B The largest volume of air which can be expired after the deepest possible inspiration.
C The amount of air moving in and out of the lungs in one minute.
D The amount of air that stays in the lungs after the maximum expiration.

Answer: ______________ (1 mark)

2 Which of the following would you expect to happen during an aerobic training session?

A Oxygen and carbon dioxide level in the body drop
B The oxygen debt would decrease
C The need for oxygen is reduced
D Glucose levels would drop (1 mark)

CHAPTER 10 (A HEALTHY, ACTIVE LIFESTYLE AND YOUR MUSCULAR SYSTEM)

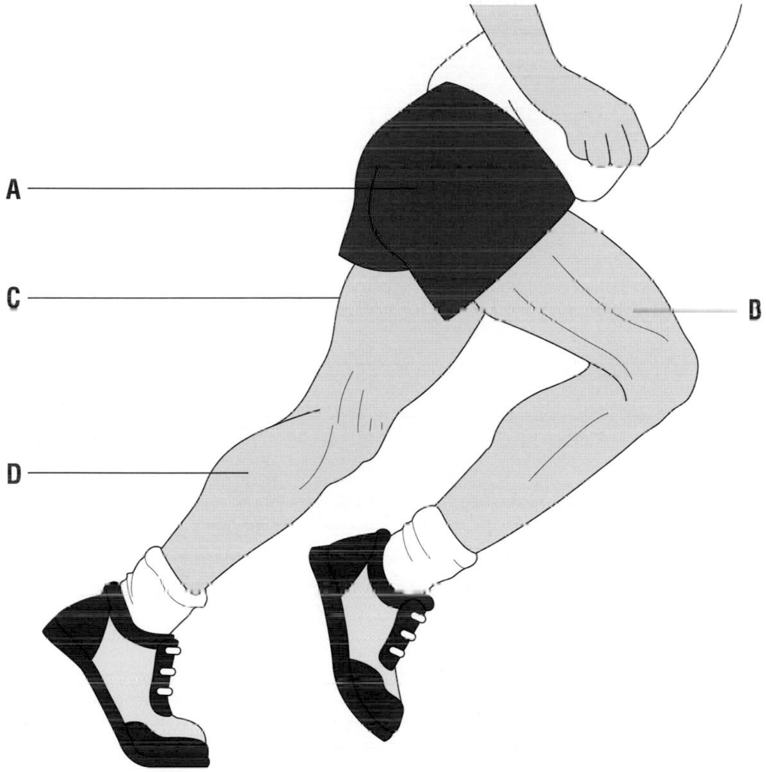

Figure 12.5 Runner's legs

1 **a)** Using Figure 12.5, which muscle, A, B or C, allows the runner to drive fowards off the toes during his running action? (1 mark)

b) Using Figure 12.5, which muscle, A, B or C, allows the runner to extend the leg at the hip? (1 mark)

c) Two of the muscles named in Table 12.7 work as an antagonistic pair. Name the two muscles.

__________________ and __________________ (1 mark)

d) Explain the term 'antagonistic pair'. (1 mark)

(Total 4 marks)

Bicep	Hamstrings	Deltoid
Quadriceps	Gluteals	

Table 12.7

Figure 12.6 is a diagram of the human muscular system from the front and the back.

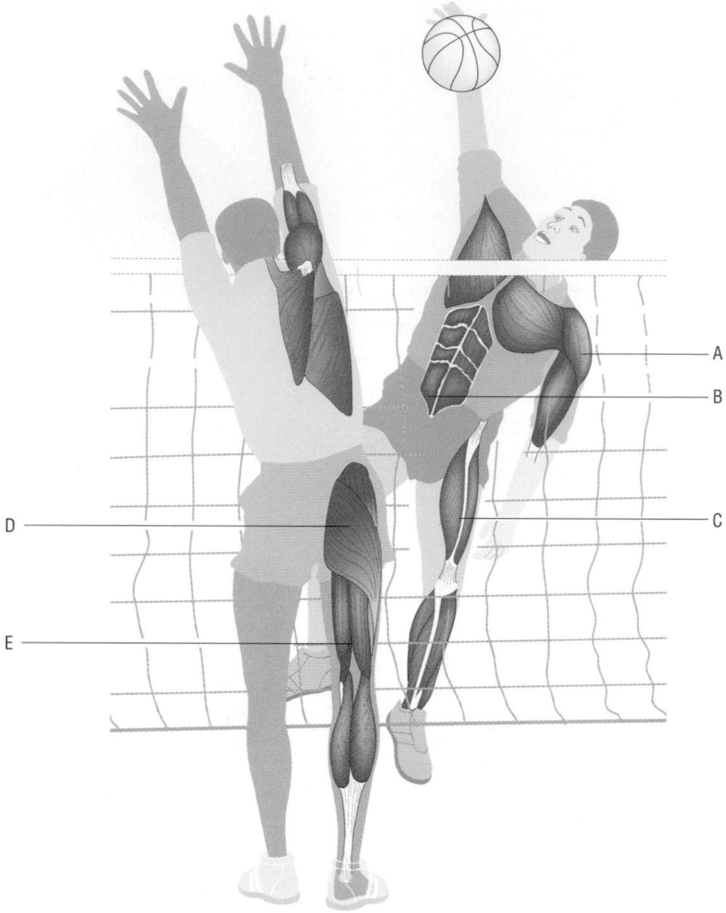

Figure 12.6 The Muscular system from front to back

2 For each of the muscles A to E (shown in Figure 12.6) select the most appropriate action from Table 12.8 to show its use in sport. Each action may only be used once. (5 marks)

(1) Arm action when preparing to start a cartwheel	(5) The upward phase of a press-up
(2) Extending the arm into the water during the front crawl	(6) Taking the leg back at the hip in preparation to kick a ball
(3) The downward phase of a press-up	(7) A pike in trampolining
(4) The follow-through after kicking a ball	(8) Legs bent in preparation for a sprint start

Table 12.8

3 The following conditions can relate to sports injuries:

A Unconscious

B No pulse

C Broken leg

D Torn ligament

Which of these is a soft tissue injury?

(1 mark)

CHAPTER 11 (AN ACTIVE HEALTHY LIFESTYLE AND YOUR SKELETAL SYSTEM)

1 Bones in other areas of the skeleton meet to form important joints, for example, the knee.

i) What type of synovial joint is the knee? (1 mark)

ii) There can be very slight rotation or sideways movement at the knee joint. What stabilises the knee joint to prevent unwanted movement? (1 mark)

iii) What are the TWO main main types of movement possible at the knee?

1 ____________________

2 ____________________

(2 marks)

(Total 4 marks)

2 What type of sports injuries or conditions have the following common symptoms?
Swelling of tissue, distortion of natural shape and difficulty in moving the injured part. ____________________ (1 mark)

3 Injuries to joints are treated usine R.I.C.E.

i) What does the **E** in R.I.C.E stand for?

____________________ (1 mark)

ii) Give **two specific** joint injuries that are treated using R.I.C.E

____________________ (2 marks)

(Total 3 marks)

REVISION CROSSWORD FOR FULL COURSE

CLUES FOR REVISION CROSSWORD FOR FULL COURSE ON PREVIOUS PAGE

Across

1. The time it takes for your body to return to its resting state is called your
2. Type of training method that allows you to vary the training methods you are using for different sessions
6. __________ are the link between the larger blood vessels
7. Type of training method arranged into stations
8. A drop in resting heart rate is an effect of __________
11. A rugby player swerving past opponents uses __________ to make sure he stays on his feet
13. This is one of the functions of the skeleton
14. Psychological benefit of taking part in physical activity
15. 220 is the recognised __________ heart rate
21. Which type of joint gives the greatest range of movement?
23. Good training method for sprinters
24. An example of protective clothing for a hockey player would be
27. Which principle of training is this an example of? 'Last time I trained I could lift 20 kg, this time I lifted 15 kg'
28. Which principle of training tells you to increase your work load gradually?
29. Which muscle extends the leg at the hip?
36. Alcohol intake slows these
39. How many components of health-related exercise are there?
40. A warm up increases body __________
41. What divides the heart in two to prevent the mixing of oxygenated and deoxygenated blood?
43. Javelin throwers need this to time the movement of their feet and arms correctly to produce a good throw
45. A dislocation is an example of a __________ injury
47. We should wash after exercise to remove __________
49. Blood doping __________ red blood cell count
52. What are used to try to reduce the chance of injury?
53. Tendons attach to __________ and bone
55. This is produced during anaerobic activity
58. What component of fitness does the sprinter need to reach the finish line first?
59. What aspect of fitness is being used? 'I hit the ball hard for a six'
60. The knee is an example of what type of joint?
61. This aspect of fitness relates to the heart, blood and blood vessels
65. Which principle of training tells you to consider the person when planning a training session?
66. If the muscles are contracting but there is no limb movement, what type of muscle contraction is taking place?
67. Extreme body type associated with sprinters
68. Water is important to reduce the chance of __________
69. The action of bringing the arm back towards the centre of the body from the side is called __________
70. If I am working at 70% of my maximum heart rate I am said to be working in my __________ of training
71. Which bone type acts as a lever?
72. Exercise is good for us because it can improve our health and __________
73. What is the name of the position you place someone in if they are breathing and have a pulse?

Down

1. This component of skill-related fitness is essential at the start of the race for swimmers and sprint runners
3. If we increase this we can increase our cardiac output
4. What phase is missing from the following exercise session? Warm up __________ Cool down
5. Which muscle pulls your arms back and in towards the body?
9. Balancing competition should make the competition __________
10. What is the missing component of a balanced diet? Fat, carbohydrates, vitamins, minerals, protein and water
12. Weight loss is an example of a __________ benefit of exercise
16. The ribs move like this when we inspire
17. Which area of the vertebral column is designed to support the body weight?
18. Increased heart rate is an __________ effect of exercise
19. __________ athletes are more likely to take EPO than performers in other types of activities
20. What is the term given to muscles that work together to allow a limb to move?
22. Reason for taking part in physical activity
25. Boxers use gloves to stop them hurting their __________ as much
26. Which chamber of the heart has the thickest muscular wall?
30. This is the place where gas exchange occurs in the lungs
31. A joint is a place where two or more bones __________
32. A strain is damage to a __________ or muscle
33. What type of blood does the left atrium receive?
34. Athletes eat carbohydrates to provide them with __________
35. Is it possible to be fit but not healthy?
37. What is being defined? 'A state of complete physical, social and mental well being'
38. Suitable training method for games players
39. What sports injury is being described? A crack or break in the bone
42. Activity that means working without oxygen
44. Regular training can increase __________ volume
48. What is the missing muscle type? Voluntary and involuntary
50. An example of an aerobic event
51. Which principle of training is missing? FIR __________ STOP
54. Which is the missing gas? Oxygen and nitrogen
56. If you need to overload you must increase the __________ of the exercise session
57. Training session without breaks
62. The scapula is an example of what type of bone?
63. Studs in boots help reduce the risk of injury by reducing the risk of the player __________
64. What is the muscle type of our skeletal muscles?

INDEX